MATH TRAILBLAZERS™

Grade 3

Unit Resource Guide
Unit 12
Dissections

SECOND EDITION

A Mathematical Journey Using Science and Language Arts

KENDALL/HUNT PUBLISHING COMPANY
4050 Westmark Drive   Dubuque, Iowa 52002

A TIMS® Curriculum
University of Illinois at Chicago

UIC The University of Illinois
at Chicago

The original edition was based on work supported by the National Science Foundation under grant No. MDR 9050226 and the University of Illinois at Chicago. Any opinions, findings, and conclusions or recommendations expressed in this publication are those of the author(s) and do not necessarily reflect the views of the granting agencies.

Printed in the United States of America

1   2   3   4   5   6   7   8   9   10   07   06   05   04   03

LETTER HOME

Dissections

Date: _____

Dear Family Member:

In this unit, *Dissections,* we take things apart to learn about them. Once a thing is taken apart, getting it back together can be a problem. Students use a set of seven shapes to solve puzzles called tangrams. Although one aim of the unit is to have fun solving geometric puzzles, there are also mathematical goals. Through making, drawing, and describing geometric shapes, students develop spatial visualization skills and the ability to think abstractly. Working the puzzles develops geometric problem-solving skills. Communication and logical thinking skills are required when students share their solutions or explain why certain problems have no solutions. Area, perimeter, angle size, symmetry, definition, classification, and congruence are other important geometric ideas that students encounter in the unit. The unit also includes gathering and organizing data and carrying out systematic searches.

The seven tans of tangrams—an old Chinese puzzle

- **Describing Shapes.** Help your child by asking him or her to identify shapes at home and to discuss the parts of common geometric shapes. Talking about the number of sides and corners of various shapes—triangles, squares, pentagons, and so on—is worthwhile. You might also make a list of examples of right angles—square corners—at home. Comparing angles to see if they are more or less than a right angle will help your child understand angular measure.

- **Math Facts.** Help your child study the multiplication facts for the twos and threes using *Triangle Flash Cards.*

Thank you for taking time to talk with your child about math.

Sincerely,

_____

UNIT OUTLINE

Dissections

Pacing Suggestions

Lesson 6 *Focus on Word Problems* is an optional lesson. These problems can be assigned as homework throughout the unit or solved in class. Since the lesson requires little teacher preparation, it is appropriate to leave for a substitute teacher.

Components Key: SG = Student Guide, DAB = Discovery Assignment Book, AB = Adventure Book, URG = Unit Resource Guide, and DPP = Daily Practice and Problems

	Sessions	Description	Supplies
LESSON 1 **Tangrams** SG pages 158–165 DAB page 185 URG pages 17–31 DPP A–D	2	**ACTIVITY:** Students explore tangram puzzles—those in which pieces are joined edge to edge. Students solve several puzzles, discuss why others are unsolvable, and design their own puzzles.	• sets of tangram pieces • envelopes • rulers
LESSON 2 **Building with Triangles** SG pages 166–169 DAB pages 187–188 URG pages 32–46 DPP E–F	1–2	**ACTIVITY:** Students make shapes by putting two or three isosceles right triangles together edge to edge. The shapes are traced on paper and measured, described, and analyzed.	• scissors • centimeter rulers • envelopes • markers or crayons • small triangles from tangram sets
LESSON 3 **Building with Four Triangles** SG pages 170–172 URG pages 47–60 DPP G–J	2	**ACTIVITY:** This activity extends the previous activity. Shapes that can be made by putting together four isosceles right triangles edge to edge are investigated. **ASSESSMENT PAGES:** *Three Tans,* Unit Resource Guide, pages 56–57.	• scissors • centimeter rulers • envelopes • sets of tangram pieces • paper

	Sessions	Description	Supplies
LESSON 4 **Dissection Puzzles** SG pages 173–175 DAB page 189 URG pages 61–68 DPP K–L	1	**ACTIVITY:** Students solve puzzles that require dissecting figures in specific ways. In each puzzle, they are given a set of pieces which they put together edge to edge to make various shapes.	• scissors
LESSON 5 **Hex** DAB page 191 URG pages 69–73 DPP M–N	1	**GAME:** Students play a geometric game similar to tic-tac-toe or "boxes." Later, this game will be adapted to provide practice in estimation and mental computation.	• beans or other small markers
LESSON 6		– OPTIONAL LESSON –	
Focus on Word Problems SG pages 176–177 URG pages 74–77	1	**OPTIONAL ACTIVITY:** Students solve problems that involve addition, subtraction, multiplication, or division.	• rulers

---

CONNECTIONS

A current list of connections is available at www.mathtrailblazers.com. Detailed information on software titles can be found in Section 13 of the Teacher Implementation Guide.

Literature   **Suggested Title**

■ Tompert, Ann. *Grandfather Tang's Story.* Crown Publishers, Inc., New York, 1990.

Software

■ *Math Munchers Deluxe* provides practice in basic facts, angles, and identifying geometric shapes in an arcade-like game.

■ *National Library of Virtual Manipulatives* website (http://matti.usu.edu) allows students to work with manipulatives including geoboards and tangrams.

■ *Shape Up!* is a geometry program that contains five sets of shapes that students can manipulate and explore.

Dissections

Taking something apart—dissecting it—is a good way to learn about it. We learn what the parts are, how they fit together, and how they relate to one another. Whether we want to learn about frogs, car engines, or squares, taking our subject apart is a good beginning.

Once a thing is taken apart, of course, getting it back together may be problematic. Our unit begins with a series of such problems: What figures can be made with a given set of pieces? In the first lesson students make shapes with the seven tangram pieces. In the next two activities, *Building with Triangles* and *Building with Four Triangles,* the pieces are isosceles right triangles. In these three activities, the pieces must be joined edge to edge, a restriction that may inhibit artistry, but that increases the mathematical content. The unit also includes *Dissection Puzzles,* a game, *Hex,* and a set of word problems.

School Geometry: Holistic to Analytic

Many students perceive geometric shapes as undifferentiated wholes. They recognize squares and triangles, and they may even be able to use terms like *rhombus* or *trapezoid;* but they are probably not aware of the parts of those shapes or of relationships between those parts. Such students do not realize that a square has four sides and four corners or that the angles are right angles and the sides are equal. They know a triangle is not a square, but cannot compare and contrast the two shapes; they do not discriminate the parts of the geometric whole. We may say that such students view shapes holistically.

A more advanced understanding requires discerning the parts of shapes and recognizing relationships among those parts. Drawing, measuring, and describing shapes can help develop this understanding. So also can breaking shapes down into their components and analyzing them so that their parts and properties are explicit—our word *analysis* comes from the Greek for "a breaking up." Developing this more analytic understanding is the key aim of this unit.

The levels of geometric understanding—and several more advanced stages—were first identified in the late 1950s by two Dutch mathematics educators, Pierre M. van Hiele and Dina van Hiele-Geldof. Mary Crowley discusses this in her article "The van Hiele

Model of the Development of Geometric Thought." (See *Resources.*)

Dissections

A **dissection** is literally a cutting into pieces. In mathematics, the things being cut into pieces are usually geometric figures. This unit focuses on dissections of plane (two-dimensional) figures.

Dissections are a rich source of puzzles. Jigsaw puzzles are a kind of dissection, although not a very mathematical one. Tangram puzzles are also dissections, again not necessarily mathematical unless certain restrictions are imposed.

The classic dissection puzzle requires rearranging pieces from one shape to make another shape. Usually, a solution that uses fewer pieces is considered more elegant. Figure 1 shows such a puzzle: Can you cut the square into two pieces that exactly cover the triangle?

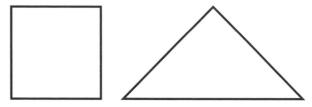

Figure 1: *A dissection puzzle*

Such puzzles can be extremely challenging. For example, can you dissect the square in Figure 2 so that the pieces exactly cover the irregular hexagon?

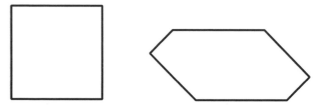

Figure 2: *A harder dissection puzzle*

The dissections in this unit, fortunately, are not nearly as hard as this one. A good puzzle, however, should be challenging, or it's no fun.

Words, Words, Words

Vocabulary boosting is not a major goal of *Math Trailblazers™,* but effective communication is, and words are important for that. Too often, traditional mathematics texts turn geometry into a dreary parade of terms and definitions. Appropriate terminology can enhance both communication and understanding; children also enjoy learning and using fancy words. The issue is balance; your professional judgment is required.

The Key Vocabulary section in the Lesson Guides lists minimal requirements. We cannot, for example, imagine talking about the parts of a triangle unless *side* and *corner* are understood. Other technical terms are used in the lessons—e.g., hexagon, trapezoid, quadrilateral—but are not as critical. We leave to your discretion the degree of familiarity you want your students to have with such terms.

When you talk about vocabulary with your students, distinguish mathematical English from everyday English. In mathematics, we often seize upon everyday terms and give them precise meanings that may differ from common meanings. Then, ironically, we complain loudly when the terms are used in their everyday sense. In everyday language, for example, a square is not a rectangle—it's a square. For most people, "rectangle" means "nonsquare rectangle." When we insist that "A square is a rectangle," students who are thinking only of vernacular meanings may come to the conclusion that mathematics is nonsense. By distinguishing mathematical usage from everyday usage, this outcome may be avoided.

Remember also that communication is more than vocabulary. Several times in this unit, for example, students are asked to explain how they know that all shapes that can be made with a given number of triangles have been identified. At other times, students are asked to describe how they solved a problem. Effective mathematical communication includes clearly describing procedures and results and arguing convincingly.

Tangrams and the Edge-to-Edge Rule

Tangram puzzles are quite popular. The majority of tangram designs are renderings of animals, flowers, people, or other real objects. In most tangram puzzles, the only rules for making shapes is that the tangram pieces must touch without overlapping. In some of the activities in this unit we introduce another rule, the "edge-to-edge" rule. This rule requires that the edge of one tangram piece exactly match the edge of the adjacent tangram piece. This restriction limits the space needed to work with the tangram pieces and makes problems more interesting and manageable.

Some of the popular literature on tangrams states that they were invented thousands of years ago. This is probably untrue. It is likely that they are only a few hundred years old, not a few thousand. (On the other hand, magic squares, introduced in Unit 2, *Strategies: An Assessment Unit,* really are ancient.)

Resources

- Coffin, Stewart T. *The Puzzling World of Polyhedral Dissections.* Oxford University Press, Oxford, 1990.
- Crowley, Mary L. "The van Hiele Model of the Development of Geometric Thought." In Mary M. Lindquist (Ed.), *Learning and Teaching Geometry, K–12: 1987 Yearbook.* The National Council of Teachers of Mathematics, Reston, VA.
- Dudeney, Henry E. *Amusements in Mathematics.* Dover Publications, New York, 1970.
- Gardner, Martin. *The 2nd Scientific American Book of Mathematical Puzzles and Diversions.* University of Chicago Press, Chicago, IL, 1987.
- Loyd, Sam, and Peter Van Note (Ed.). *The 8th Book of Tan: 700 Tangrams.* Dover Publications, New York, 1968.
- Read, Ronald C. *Tangrams—330 Puzzles.* Dover Publications, New York, 1980.
- Slocum, Jerry, and Jack Botermans. *Puzzles Old and New: How to Make and Solve Them.* University of Washington Press, Seattle, 1986.

Assessment Indicators

- Can students analyze and describe 2-dimensional shapes using their properties (number of sides, corners, and right angles)?
- Can students measure area and perimeter of 2-dimensional shapes?
- Can students identify congruent shapes?
- Can students identify line symmetry?
- Can students use geometric concepts and skills to solve problems and communicate their reasoning?
- Do students demonstrate fluency for the multiplication facts for the 2s and 3s?

OBSERVATIONAL ASSESSMENT RECORD

(A1) Can students analyze and describe 2-dimensional shapes using their properties (number of sides, corners, and right angles)?

(A2) Can students measure area and perimeter of 2-dimensional shapes?

(A3) Can students identify congruent shapes?

(A4) Can students identify line symmetry?

(A5) Can students use geometric concepts and skills to solve problems and communicate their reasoning?

(A6) Do students demonstrate fluency for the multiplication facts for the 2s and 3s?

(A7) _____

Name	A1	A2	A3	A4	A5	A6	A7	Comments
1.								
2.								
3.								
4.								
5.								
6.								
7.								
8.								
9.								
10.								
11.								
12.								
13.								

Name	A1	A2	A3	A4	A5	A6	A7	Comments
14.								
15.								
16.								
17.								
18.								
19.								
20.								
21.								
22.								
23.								
24.								
25.								
26.								
27.								
28.								
29.								
30.								
31.								
32.								

Daily Practice and Problems

Dissections

Two Daily Practice and Problems (DPP) items are included for each class session listed in the Unit Outline. A Scope and Sequence Chart for the DPP can be found in the *Teacher Implementation Guide*.

A DPP Menu for Unit 12

Icons in the Teacher Notes column designate the subject matter of each DPP item. The first item for each class session is always a Bit and the second is either a Task or Challenge. Each item falls into one or more of the categories listed below. A menu of the DPP items for Unit 12 follows.

N Number Sense	**⊠** Computation	**🕐** Time	**⬡** Geometry
F, J	E–H, J	I	B, D, L, N
Math Facts	**$** Money	**Measurement**	**Data**
A, C, J, K, M	F	N	

Practicing and Assessing the Multiplication Facts

By the end of third grade, students are expected to demonstrate fluency with the multiplication facts. In Units 3–10, students explored patterns in multiplication and developed strategies for learning the multiplication facts. In this unit, they study the twos and threes.

DPP Bit A introduces the *Triangle Flash Cards: 2s and 3s*. Flash cards are in the *Discovery Assignment Book* immediately following the Home Practice. They can also be found in the Generic Section of the *Unit Resource Guide*. In Unit 12, DPP items C, J, and K provide practice with multiplication facts in these groups and Bit M is a quiz.

For information on the study of the multiplication facts in Grade 3, see the DPP Guide for Unit 3. For a detailed explanation of our approach to learning and assessing the math facts in Grade 3, see the *Grade 3 Facts Resource Guide* and for information for Grades K–5, see the TIMS Tutor: *Math Facts* in the *Teacher Implementation Guide*.

Students may solve the items individually, in groups, or as a class. The items may also be assigned for homework.

Student Questions	Teacher Notes

A Triangle Flash Cards: 2s and 3s

With a partner, use your *Triangle Flash Cards* to quiz each other on the multiplication facts for the twos and threes. One partner covers the corner containing the highest number. This number will be the product. The second person multiplies the two uncovered numbers.

Separate the used cards into three piles: those facts you know and can answer quickly, those that you can figure out with a strategy, and those that you need to learn. Practice the last two piles again and then make a list of the facts you need to practice at home for homework.

Circle the facts you know and can answer quickly on your *Multiplication Facts I Know* chart.

TIMS Bit

The *Triangle Flash Cards* follow the Home Practice for this unit in the *Discovery Assignment Book*. Remind students to take home the list of the facts they need to practice and their *Triangle Flash Cards* to study with a family member.

Have students record the facts they know well on their *Multiplication Facts I Know* charts. Students should circle the facts they know and can answer quickly. Since these charts can also be used as multiplication tables, students should have them available to use as needed.

Inform students when the quiz on the 2s and 3s will be given. This quiz appears in TIMS Bit M.

Student Questions	Teacher Notes

 Right Angles 1

1. How many right (square) angles do you see inside the shapes below? Circle them as you count.

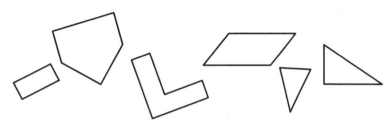

2. Tell how you decided which angles were right angles.

TIMS Task

1. the rectangle (4), pentagon (3), hexagon (5), right triangle (1); total is 13

2. Answers will vary. Examples: "I used the corner of my ruler." "I used the corner of a sheet of paper."

C Using Twos

Do these problems in your head. Write only the answers.

A. $2 \times 9 =$ B. $3 \times 20 =$

C. $2 \times 100 =$ D. $8 \times 2 =$

E. $5 \times 20 =$ F. $20 \times 2 =$

G. $4 \times 2 =$ H. $6 \times 2 =$

I. $2 \times 7 =$ J. $2 \times 0 =$

TIMS Bit

Ask students what strategies they use for solving these problems.

A. 18		B. 60	
C. 200		D. 16	
E. 100		F. 40	
G. 8		H. 12	
I. 14		J. 0	

D Right Angles 2

Find at least six right (square) angles in your classroom. Draw and label each object. Also, show where the right angle is on each.

TIMS Task

Some possible objects: the chalkboard, a book, a ruler, the teacher's desktop, a calendar, the top of a tissue box.

Student Questions	Teacher Notes

 Chapter Books

1. Ann is reading a book that has about 400 pages. Each chapter in her book has about 25 pages. About how many chapters are there?

2. Marta's book has chapters that are about 15 pages long. Her book has 20 chapters. About how long is Marta's book?

TIMS Bit

1. 16 chapters. Students may count by 25s or repeatedly subtract 25 on the calculator. Relating 25 to 25¢ and 400 to $4 may be helpful for students trying to do the division in their heads.

2. 300 pages. Discuss strategies such as using a calculator or using the patterns in multiplying with multiples of 10.

 Tricky Change

Sally has a pocket of pennies, dimes, and quarters. She reaches in and pulls out four coins.

1. What amount of money might Sally have? List three different amounts.

2. What is the least she could have?

3. What is the most?

4. Could she have pulled out 12 cents? 8 cents? 25 cents? 46 cents?

TIMS Task

1. There are many possible answers. Three examples are: 40 cents (4 dimes), 52 cents (2 quarters and 2 pennies), 85 cents (3 quarters and 1 dime), 13 cents (1 dime and 3 pennies).

2. 4 pennies; 4 cents

3. 4 quarters; $1.00

4. No, No, No, Yes

Student Questions	Teacher Notes
Subtraction	**TIMS Bit**

Complete the following problems. Use pencil and paper or mental math to find the answers.

1. 594
  − 225

2. 6784
  − 2387

3. 231
  − 179

4. 602
  − 199

Explain your strategy for Question 3.

TIMS Bit

1. 369

2. 4397

3. 52

4. 403

Possible strategy: Count up 1 to 180, 20 to 200, 30 to 230, and move to 231.

1 + 20 + 30 + 1 = 52

 Larry the Lizard Show

Use the Lizardland picture in the *Student Guide* in Unit 11 to solve the following problems. 178 people attended the 10 A.M. show. 284 people attended the noon show.

1. How many more people attended the noon show than the 10 A.M. show?

2. How many people attended the first two shows?

3. How many empty seats were there during the first two shows?

TIMS Task

Students may use base-ten pieces or paper and pencil to find the answers.

1. 106 people

2. 462 people

3. (300 + 300) − (178 + 284) = 138 empty seats

Student Questions	Teacher Notes

 Bus Stop

Starting at 7:00 in the morning, a bus passes Ellen's stop every 15 minutes.

1. How many minutes must Ellen wait for the next bus if she gets to the stop at 9:05?

2. Will a bus come at 4:20 in the afternoon? How do you know?

TIMS Bit

You can work with a clock, showing the position of the minute hand as students count.

1. 10 minutes

2. No. 4:20 does not end in :00, :15, :30, or :45.

J **Story Solving**

1. $3 \times 9 = ?$ Write a story and draw a picture about 3×9. Write a number sentence on your picture.

2. $3 \times \frac{1}{2} = ?$ Write a story, and draw a picture about $3 \times \frac{1}{2}$. Write a number sentence on your picture.

TIMS Task

1. 27; Stories will vary.

2. $1\frac{1}{2}$; Students may wish to share their stories with the class. If there is a computer with a drawing program available, students may choose to draw their picture and tell their story on the computer.

K **Using Threes**

Do these problems in your head. Write only the answers.

A. $3 \times 5 =$ B. $7 \times 3 =$

C. $9 \times 3 =$ D. $3 \times 2 =$

E. $10 \times 3 =$ F. $3 \times 6 =$

G. $4 \times 3 =$ H. $3 \times 3 =$

I. $3 \times 1 =$ J. $8 \times 3 =$

Describe a strategy for 8×3.

TIMS Bit

Ask students what strategies they use for solving these problems.

A. 15   B. 21
C. 27   D. 6
E. 30   F. 18
G. 12   H. 9
I. 3   J. 24

Two possible strategies: skip count by 3s; $4 \times 3 = 12$, so 8×3 is double 12, or 24.

Dissection Puzzle 1

Trace and cut out the following triangles.

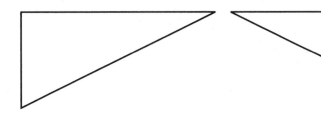

1. Put them edge to edge to make a rectangle.

2. Put them edge to edge to make a triangle.

3. Make four other shapes.

TIMS Task

You may wish to have students draw the shapes.

Ask students to describe all their shapes. How are they alike? How do they differ?

M **Quiz on 2s and 3s**

A. $4 \times 2 =$ B. $3 \times 2 =$

C. $5 \times 3 =$ D. $2 \times 10 =$

E. $6 \times 3 =$ F. $2 \times 5 =$

G. $10 \times 3 =$ H. $7 \times 2 =$

I. $8 \times 3 =$ J. $3 \times 3 =$

K. $8 \times 2 =$ L. $2 \times 2 =$

M. $9 \times 2 =$ N. $6 \times 2 =$

O. $3 \times 7 =$ P. $4 \times 3 =$

Q. $3 \times 9 =$ R. $3 \times 1 =$

TIMS Bit

This quiz is on the second group of multiplication facts, the 2s and 3s. We recommend 5 minutes for this quiz. You might want to allow students to change pens after the time is up and complete the remaining problems in a different color.

After students take the quiz, have them update their *Multiplication Facts I Know* charts.

Dissection Puzzle 2

1. Trace and cut out the shapes below.

2. Find all shapes that can be made by putting the three pieces edge to edge. Trace them on a piece of paper.

3. Make a data table that shows the area, perimeter, and lines of symmetry for each shape. Measure in square inches and inches.

TIMS Challenge

There are 5 non-congruent shapes.

A.

B.

C.

D.

E.

Discuss whether two shapes are the same. If you can turn or flip a shape and match another, the two shapes are the same. Some of the shapes can be made in more than one way. For example, shape D can be made as follows:

Shape	Perimeter (inches)	Number of lines of symmetry	Area (sq. inches)
A	10	2	4
B	8	4	4
C	10	0	4
D	10	1	4
E	10	0	4

LESSON GUIDE

Tangrams

Students attempt to cover a series of figures with all or some of the seven tangram pieces. Some of the figures are possible to cover; others are not. For those that cannot be covered, students explain why not. Then, students make their own tangram puzzles and share them with other students.

Key Content

- Representing shapes with tangrams, drawings, and words.
- Developing spatial visualization skills.
- Using geometric concepts (area and angle size) and skills to solve problems and communicate reasoning.

Key Vocabulary

angle
area
edge
tangram

A. Triangle Flash Cards: 2s and 3s

(URG p. 10)

With a partner, use your *Triangle Flash Cards* to quiz each other on the multiplication facts for the twos and threes. One partner covers the corner containing the highest number. This number will be the product. The second person multiplies the two uncovered numbers.

Separate the used cards into three piles: those facts you know and can answer quickly, those that you can figure out with a strategy, and those that you need to learn. Practice the last two piles again and then make a list of the facts you need to practice at home for homework.

Circle the facts you know and can answer quickly on your *Multiplication Facts I Know* chart.

C. Using Twos (URG p. 11)

Do these problems in your head. Write only the answers.

A. $2 \times 9 =$ B. $3 \times 20 =$

C. $2 \times 100 =$ D. $8 \times 2 =$

E. $5 \times 20 =$ F. $20 \times 2 =$

G. $4 \times 2 =$ H. $6 \times 2 =$

I. $2 \times 7 =$ J. $2 \times 0 =$

DPP Tasks are on page 24. Suggestions for using the DPPs are on page 24.

Materials List

Print Materials for Students

	Math Facts and Daily Practice and Problems	Activity	Homework
Student Books — Student Guide		*Tangrams* Pages 158–165	
Student Books — Discovery Assignment Book		*Making a Tangram Puzzle* Page 185	Home Practice Part 1 Page 178, *Triangle Flash Cards: 2s* Page 181, and *Triangle Flash Cards: 3s* Page 183
Teacher Resources — Facts Resource Guide ⊙	DPP Items 12A & 12C Use *Triangle Flash Cards: 2s* and *Triangle Flash Cards: 3s* to review the multiplication facts for the 2s and 3s.		
Teacher Resources — Unit Resource Guide ⊙	DPP Items A–D Pages 10–11	*Tangram Pieces Master* Page 27, 1 per student pair (optional)	

⊙ *available on Teacher Resource CD*

All Transparency Masters, Blackline Masters, and Assessment Blackline Masters in the Unit Resource Guide are on the Teacher Resource CD.

Supplies for Each Student

set of tangram pieces (See Before the Activity)
envelope for storing tangram pieces
envelope for storing flash cards
ruler

Materials for the Teacher

Hints for Puzzling Tangrams Transparency Master (Unit Resource Guide) Page 28

Before the Activity

Each student needs one set of tangram pieces. Tangram pieces based on a 4-inch square are commercially available. If you do not wish to purchase the tangram pieces, you can make your own. Make copies of the *Tangram Pieces Master* on sturdy material like tagboard, card stock, or construction paper. We recommend that you or another adult cut the tangram pieces apart so that they are accurate.

TIMS Tip

If you purchase tangram pieces, the longest side of the largest triangle should be 4 inches long. However, many commercially available tangram pieces are a little smaller and will not fit exactly in the tangrams we have provided. You may want to reduce the tangram puzzles slightly on a copier or tell students that tangram pieces must fit inside the outline of the tangram rather than on the lines.

Developing the Activity

Part 1. Introducing Tangrams with Tangram Animals and More Tangram Animals

One way to introduce tangrams is to read the first *Tangrams* Activity Page in the *Student Guide* as a class. This page introduces the seven tangram pieces and explains a general rule for making tangrams.

Another way to introduce tangrams is by reading the book *Grandfather Tang's Story* by Ann Tompert. In this book, a grandfather tells a fairy tale and illustrates it with tangrams.

Yet another way to begin is to make a tangram animal or other design on the overhead and then ask students to make and share their own tangrams. Provide a period of relatively unstructured work to give students an opportunity to explore ways to use tangram pieces.

Explore dissections by using tangram pieces to cover the animal shapes on the Tangram Animals and More Tangram Animals sections of the *Student Guide*. Have students work individually or in pairs to solve the tangrams. In Tangram Animals, students use fewer than seven tangram pieces and in More Tangram Animals, students use all seven tangram pieces.

Content Note

Usually the word *tangram* refers to the puzzle and *tans* or *tangram pieces* refer to the seven pieces used to make the puzzle. However, the word *tangram* is frequently used to describe both the pieces and the puzzle.

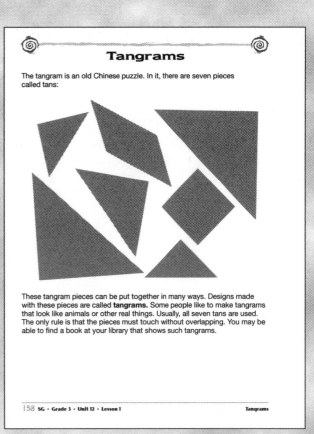

Student Guide - Page 158

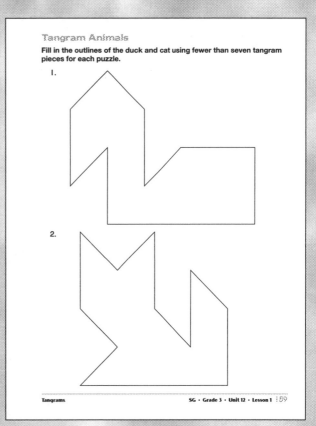

Student Guide - Page 159

More Tangram Animals

Fill in the outlines of the horse and giraffe using all seven tangram pieces.

3.

160 **SG · Grade 3 · Unit 12 · Lesson 1**   **Tangrams**

Student Guide - Page 160

4.

Tangrams   **SG · Grade 3 · Unit 12 · Lesson 1** 161

Student Guide - Page 161

Part 2. Puzzling Tangrams

In the Puzzling Tangrams section, students try to cover six shapes with the seven tangram pieces. Three of these shapes (shapes 5, 6, and 8) are possible. Shapes 7, 9, and 10 cannot be covered exactly with the seven tangram pieces. Have students work in pairs to solve each problem and compare solutions with another group.

Some students may give up after a short time. Encourage them to persist. Interesting problems require perseverance. If some students need a hint, suggest that they try to place the large triangles first. Also, they may need to flip the parallelogram.

Question 5 asks students to make a square using all seven tangram pieces. Reassembling the seven tangram pieces into a square is difficult. On this activity page, an outline of the square and a background inch grid are provided to simplify the problem.

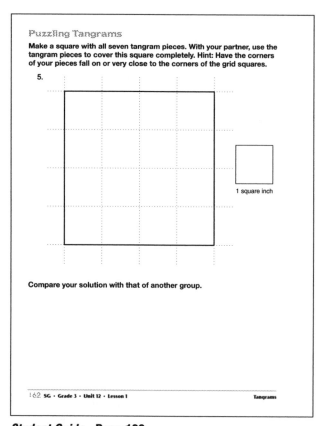

Puzzling Tangrams

Make a square with all seven tangram pieces. With your partner, use the tangram pieces to cover this square completely. Hint: Have the corners of your pieces fall on or very close to the corners of the grid squares.

5.

1 square inch

Compare your solution with that of another group.

162 **SG · Grade 3 · Unit 12 · Lesson 1**   **Tangrams**

Student Guide - Page 162

20   URG · Grade 3 · Unit 12 · Lesson 1

Some tangrams, such as the square, can be quite challenging. A number of strategies can be used for solving tangrams. The most obvious one is looking for angles that match. For example, if the shape has a square corner, look for one or more shapes that will make a square corner. A second strategy is to look at the lengths of the sides of the tangram pieces. There are four different lengths: 2 inches, 4 inches, about 1.41 inches, and about 2.83 inches. The square is 4 inches by 4 inches so the only way to get a 4-inch side is by using one 4-inch length or two 2-inch lengths. This observation makes the square puzzle much easier, so we recommend not giving it until students have worked hard at their puzzles.

For **Question 5** if turns and flips are not counted as different, there is only one solution to the tangram square. If they are counted as different, then the eight solutions in Figure 3 are possible.

> **IMS Tip**
>
> Note that the *Tangram Pieces Master* shows one way to make a square with the tangram pieces.

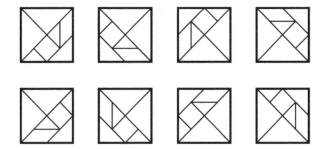

Figure 3: *Eight tangram squares*

To help students solve the puzzles in **Questions 5** and **6,** you can give them an additional hint by using the *Hints for Puzzling Tangrams* Transparency Master. This transparency gives the location of one of the tangram pieces for the first two puzzles.

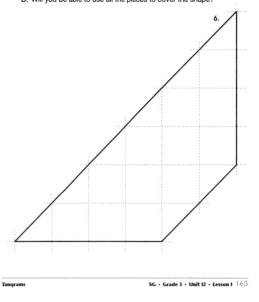

Student Guide - Page 163

Try to use all seven pieces to cover each shape in Questions 6–10. Some of the shapes can be covered with the pieces and some cannot. If you cannot cover a shape exactly using all the pieces, explain why. As you try to solve the puzzles, use the questions below to help.

A. What is the area of the square in Question 5? This is the total area of all your tangram pieces.
B. What is the area of the shape you are trying to cover?
C. Can you find a tangram piece to fit in each corner of the shape?
D. Will you be able to use all the pieces to cover the shape?

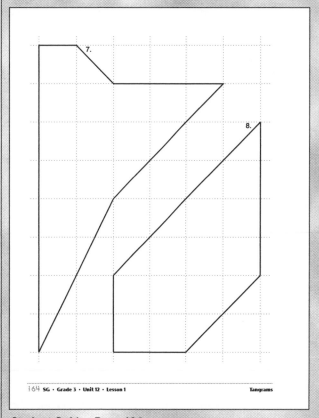

Student Guide - Page 164

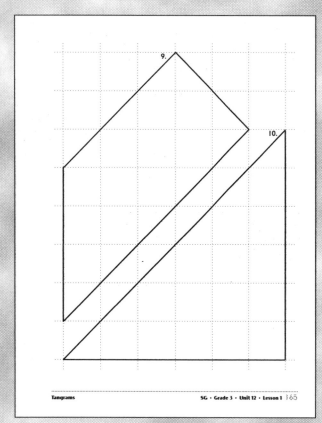

Student Guide - Page 165

If students have difficulty with **Question 9,** Figure 4 shows the location of one tangram piece or you may refer to the Answer Key for other hints.

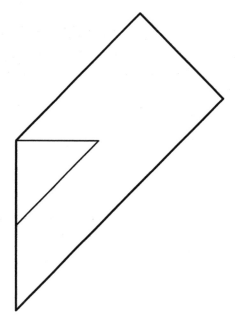

Figure 4: *Hint for **Question 9***

In addition to geometric problem solving, the Puzzling Tangrams section raises three important issues: impossible problems, mathematical reasoning, and communication.

Students may not realize that not every problem has a solution. Accordingly, they may waste time and effort attempting the impossible—i.e., trying to cover shapes 7, 8, and 10 with the tangram pieces. We have provided some questions to guide students as they work on **Questions 6–10.** After reading and discussing the questions before **Question 6,** students should see that a tangram cannot be covered unless the area of the tangram is 16 square inches and the angles are the right size(s). By referring to the square in **Question 5,** students can see that the total area of the seven tangram pieces is 16 square inches.

> **📓 Journal Prompt**
>
> Students can write a paragraph to convince a friend that it is impossible to cover shapes 7, 8, and 10 with the seven tangram pieces. Encourage the use of diagrams and mathematical concepts and terminology. Before the writing begins, you might brainstorm a list of words that may be useful.

There is a big difference between realizing that one cannot solve a problem and realizing that no one can ever solve the problem. The former realization is personal; the latter involves logical reasoning and mathematical arguments. To conclude, for example, that a shape's area precludes its ever being covered with the seven tangram pieces is a significant step on the road to higher level thinking.

Communication is vitally important in such problems. Mathematical arguments are tested and verified through a social process: The reasoning is made public and is accepted or rejected by a mathematical community. Accordingly, once students find a shape impossible to cover, they are to explain why in a way that persuades others. Using mathematical concepts and terminology can make explanations clearer and more convincing.

Part 3. Making a Tangram Puzzle

In this final section, students create their own tangrams on the *Making a Tangram Puzzle* Activity Page in the *Discovery Assignment Book* and draw solutions for them on a separate sheet of paper. Remind students to use all seven tangram pieces and that pieces should not overlap. After creating their own tangrams, give students an opportunity to trade puzzles with their classmates.

TIMS Tip

Tracing around tangram pieces may be difficult for students because the pieces tend to slide as students move their pencil around them. It may be easier for students to place a dot at each corner of the tangram piece and connect the dots with a ruler.

Name _____ Date _____

Making a Tangram Puzzle

Make up your own tangram puzzle.

- Create a design using all seven tangram pieces.
- Make sure your pieces touch without overlapping.
- Then, make an outline of your design in the space below.
- Trade tangrams with a friend. Try to solve each other's tangrams.

Tangrams   DAB · Grade 3 · Unit 12 · Lesson 1 185

Discovery Assignment Book - Page 185

Daily Practice and Problems: Tasks for Lesson 1

B. Task: Right Angles 1 (URG p. 11)

1. How many right (square) angles do you see inside the shapes below? Circle them as you count.

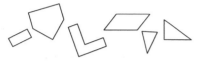

2. Tell how you decided which angles were right angles.

D. Task: Right Angles 2 (URG p. 11)

Find at least six right (square) angles in your classroom. Draw and label each object. Also, show where the right angle is on each.

Name_____ Date _____

Unit 12: Home Practice

Part 1

Estimate to be sure your answers are reasonable.

1.	285	2.	285	3.	872	4.	872
	+300		+318		−400		−490

5. Explain your estimation strategy for Question 4.

6. Marie has 748 marbles in her collection. She wants 1000. How many more marbles does she need?

Part 2

1.	115	2.	127	3.	280	4.	325
	+27		+74		−33		−76

5. Explain a strategy for using mental math for Question 3.

6. Ted read a book for 43 minutes on Saturday and 29 minutes on Sunday.
   A. Did Ted read for more than one hour? Explain how you know.

   B. How many minutes did Ted read? _____

178 DAB · Grade 3 · Unit 12   DISSECTIONS

Discovery Assignment Book - Page 178

Suggestions for Teaching the Lesson

Math Facts

DPP Bit A introduces *Triangle Flash Cards* for the multiplication facts for the twos and threes. Bit C provides practice with the multiplication facts for the twos.

Homework and Practice

- DPP Tasks B and D review identifying right angles. This review will help with concepts in Lesson 2.

- After working on some of the shapes in *Questions 5–10* in class, students can finish the activity at home. To do this, they will need a set of tangram pieces (commercially bought or made using the *Tangram Pieces Master*). Stress that not every shape can be covered so that you do not get notes from frustrated parents about impossible homework.

- The *Making a Tangram Puzzle* Activity Page is also suitable for homework. Each student will need a set of tangram pieces. Encourage students to ask a family member to try to solve his or her puzzle.

- Students take home their *Triangle Flash Cards: 2s* and *3s* to study with a family member. The *Triangle Flash Cards: 2s* and *3s* can be found immediately following the Home Practice in the *Discovery Assignment Book*.

- Home Practice Part 1 provides practice with addition and subtraction computation.

Answers for Part 1 of the Home Practice can be found in the Answer Key at the end of this lesson and at the end of this unit.

Assessment

The Journal Prompt provides an opportunity to observe how students are using terminology and concepts to make explanations clear and convincing.

Extension

- **Convex Polygons.** Figure 5 shows the 13 convex polygons that can be made with the seven tangram pieces. Three of these appear in *Questions 5–10;* the other ten are also good puzzles. You can outline these on paper for students who are interested.

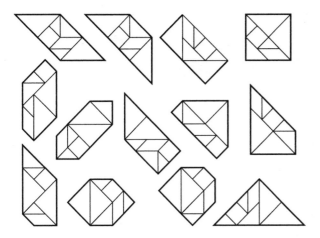

Figure 5: *Thirteen convex tangram polygons for use as extension puzzles*

- **Other Tangrams.** Provide an outline of a tangram to be covered or ask that a particular figure be made (e.g., a bird or a house). You can make up your own puzzles or find them in some of the books listed in Resources.

Literature Connection

- Tompert, Ann. *Grandfather Tang's Story.* Crown Publishers, New York, 1990.

Resources

- Crowley, Mary L. "The van Hiele Model of the Development of Geometric Thought." In Mary M. Lindquist (Ed.), *Learning and Teaching Geometry, K–12: 1987 Yearbook,* National Council of Teachers of Mathematics, Reston, VA.
- Gardner, Martin. *The 2nd Scientific American Book of Mathematical Puzzles and Diversions.* University of Chicago Press, Chicago, IL, 1987.
- Loyd, Sam, and Peter Van Note (Ed.). *The 8th Book of Tan: 700 Tangrams.* Dover Publications, New York, 1968.
- Read, Ronald C. *Tangrams—330 Puzzles.* Dover Publications, New York, 1980.
- Slocum, Jerry, and Jack Botermans. *Puzzles Old and New: How to Make and Solve Them.* University of Washington Press, Seattle, 1986.

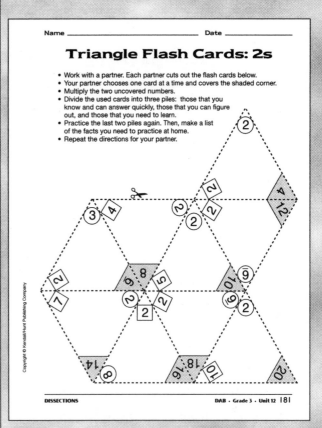

Discovery Assignment Book - Page 181

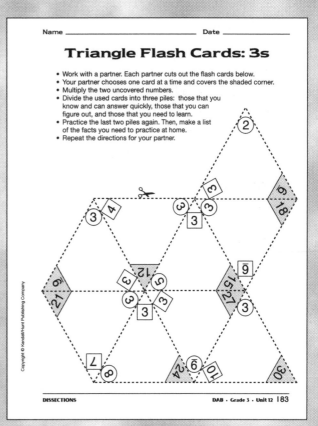

Discovery Assignment Book - Page 183

AT A GLANCE

Math Facts and Daily Practice and Problems

DPP Bit A introduces the *Triangle Flash Cards: 2s* and *3s*. Bit C provides practice with the twos. Tasks B and D review identifying right angles.

Part 1. Introducing Tangrams with Tangram Animals and More Tangram Animals

1. Introduce tangrams by reading the first *Tangrams* Activity Page as a class, reading *Grandfather Tang's Story,* or making a tangram on the overhead. Ask students to make and share their own tangrams.
2. Students find ways to cover the tangrams in the Tangram Animals and More Tangram Animals sections. *(Questions 1–4)*

Part 2. Puzzling Tangrams

1. Student pairs find and share solutions for the tangram square for *Question 5.*
2. Students read and discuss the questions that precede *Question 6.*
3. Students solve *Questions 6–10* and explain why some shapes are impossible to cover.

Part 3. Making a Tangram Puzzle

Students create their own tangrams and share them with classmates on the *Making a Tangram Puzzle* Activity Page in the *Discovery Assignment Book.*

Homework

1. Assign Home Practice Part 1.
2. Have students share the puzzle they made on the *Making a Tangram Puzzle* Activity Page with a family member.
3. Assign some of the problems in the Puzzling Tangrams section of the *Tangrams* Activity Pages in the *Student Guide.*
4. Remind students to take home their *Triangle Flash Cards* to study with a family member.

Assessment

Use the Journal Prompt as an assessment.

Notes:

Tangram Pieces Master

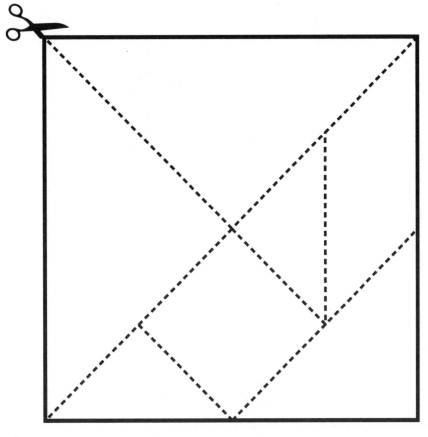

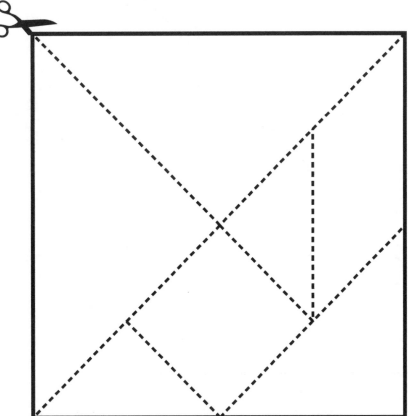

Hints for Puzzling Tangrams

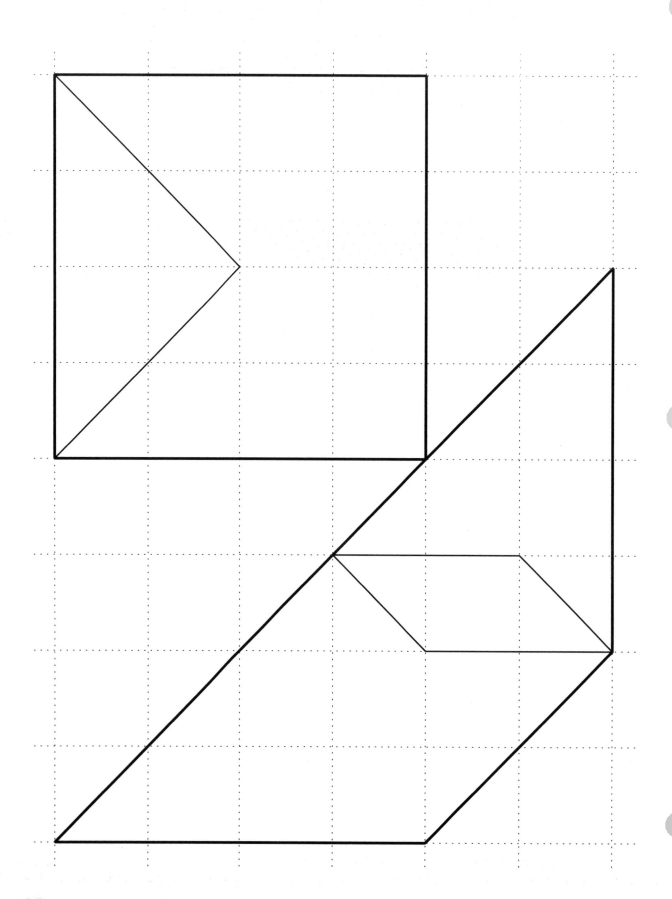

Student Guide

Questions 1–10 (SG pp. 159–165)

1.

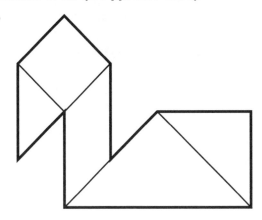

2.

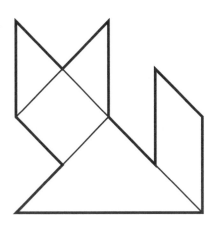

3.

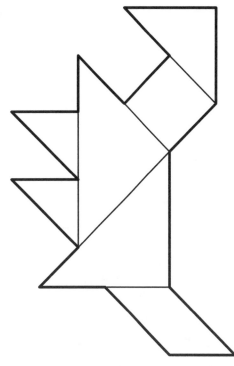

4.

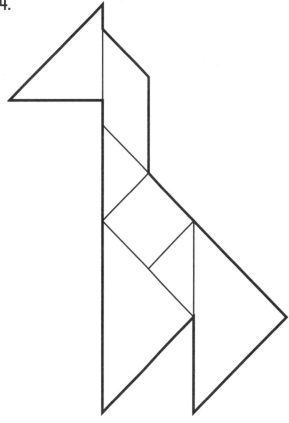

*Answers and/or discussion are included in the Lesson Guide.

**Answers for all the Home Practice in the *Discovery Assignment Book* are at the end of the unit.

5.

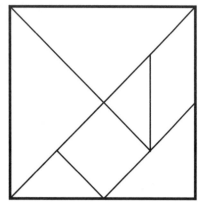

A. The area of the square in *Question 5* is 16 sq in.

B. The area of each of the three shapes in *Question 5, 6, 7,* and *9* is 16 sq in. The shape in *Question 8* is 14 sq in. The shape in *Question 10* is 18 sq in.

C. The angle at the bottom of the shape in *Question 7* cannot be matched with any tangram piece.

D. The shapes in *Questions 7, 8,* and *10* cannot be covered with all the pieces.

6. Answers may vary. One possible solution is shown below.

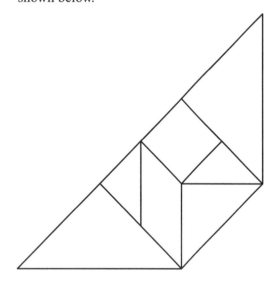

7. This puzzle is impossible. The bottom angle in this shape cannot be matched with any of the tangram pieces.

8. This shape cannot be filled using the 7 tangram pieces because the area of this shape is only 14 sq inches. The total area of the tangram pieces is 16 sq in. The shape can be covered with exactly 6 pieces. Which tan must be left out?

9. Answers may vary. Two possible solutions are shown.

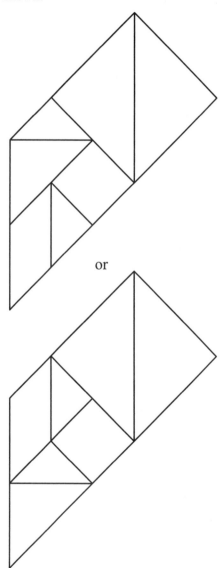

or

10. The area of this triangle is 18 sq in. It is too large to be covered by only the seven tangram pieces.

Discovery Assignment Book

****Home Practice (DAB p. 178)**

Part 1

Questions 1–6

I. 585

2. 603

3. 472

4. 382

5. Possible answer: 872 is close to 900 and 490 is close to 500. So the answer is close to $900 - 500 = 400$.

6. 252 marbles

Making a Tangram Puzzle (DAB p. 185)

Answers will vary.

---

*Answers and/or discussion are included in the Lesson Guide.

**Answers for all the Home Practice in the *Discovery Assignment Book* are at the end of the unit.

LESSON GUIDE

Building with Triangles

Estimated Class Sessions: 1–2

Students make shapes by putting two or three isosceles right triangles together edge to edge. The shapes are recorded, measured, described, and analyzed. In Lesson 3 *Building with Four Triangles,* their work is extended to four triangles.

Key Content

- Representing shapes using manipulatives, drawings, and words.

- Using flips and turns to identify shapes that are congruent.

- Analyzing and classifying shapes using their properties (number of sides, corners, right angles, and lines of symmetry).

- Measuring area and perimeter.

- Solving geometric problems and explaining the reasoning.

Key Vocabulary

congruent
corner (vertex)
line symmetry
line of symmetry
square corner (right angle)

Curriculum Sequence

Before This Unit

Line Symmetry. Students identified line symmetry in Grade 2 Unit 15.

Area and Perimeter. Students measured area in Grade 3 Unit 5. They measured perimeters of regular shapes in Unit 7 Lesson 6 *Walking around Shapes.*

After This Unit

Line Symmetry. Students will explore symmetry further in Grade 4 Unit 9.

Area and Perimeter. Students will measure area and perimeter in Grade 4 Unit 2.

Analyzing and Describing Shapes. Students will analyze and describe three-dimensional shapes in Grade 3 Unit 18.

Materials List

Print Materials for Students

	Math Facts and Daily Practice and Problems	Activity	Homework
Student Guide		*Building with Triangles* Pages 166–169	
Discovery Assignment Book		*Building with Triangles* Data Table 1 Page 187 and *Building with Triangles* Data Table 2 Page 188	Home Practice Part 2 Page 178
Unit Resource Guide	DPP Items E–F Page 12 ◎	*Lines of Symmetry* Page 42, 1 per student (optional)	

◎ *available on Teacher Resource CD*

All Transparency Masters, Blackline Masters, and Assessment Blackline Masters in the Unit Resource Guide are on the Teacher Resource CD.

Supplies for Each Student

centimeter ruler
markers or crayons
scissors

Supplies for Each Student Group

3 small triangles from 2 tangram sets
square from a set of tangrams, optional
envelope for storing triangles

Materials for the Teacher

Right Triangle Master Blackline Master (Unit Resource Guide) Page 43, one or two copies on heavy paper, optional
When Are Shapes the Same? Transparency Master (Unit Resource Guide) Page 44
Observational Assessment Record (Unit Resource Guide, Pages 7–8 and Teacher Resource CD)

Before the Activity

For this lesson, each student pair needs three isosceles right triangles with a two-inch hypotenuse as shown in Figure 6. The smallest triangles in a set of tangrams are this size. If tangrams of this size are not available, a copy of the *Right Triangle Master* Blackline Master will provide enough triangles for eight pairs of students. Since these triangles will be used for several days, the copies should be made of a sturdy material like card stock, tag board, or construction paper and students should store their triangles in envelopes.

Figure 6: *Student groups need three triangles of this size and shape to complete this lesson*

As part of this lesson, students draw lines of symmetry on the shapes they build. Second grade students using *Math Trailblazers* learned to identify shapes with line symmetry. If you have students who are new to *Math Trailblazers* who have not studied line symmetry before, use the *Lines of Symmetry* Blackline Master to prepare them for this lesson or have a class discussion about lines of symmetry.

A shape has **line symmetry** if after flipping the shape along that line, it still looks the same. You can show that a shape has line symmetry by folding the shape into two matching halves. (The halves must fold perfectly onto each other.) The fold line is called the **line of symmetry.** Students should cut out the shapes on the *Lines of Symmetry* Blackline Master and try to fold each shape into matching halves. Remind them that the fold line is called the line of symmetry and ask them to draw the lines of symmetry on the appropriate shapes. Note that a shape can have more than one line of symmetry. Students draw all the lines of symmetry they find on a shape. Figure 7 shows the lines of symmetry for shapes A and C on the *Lines of Symmetry* Blackline Master. Shape B does not have line symmetry.

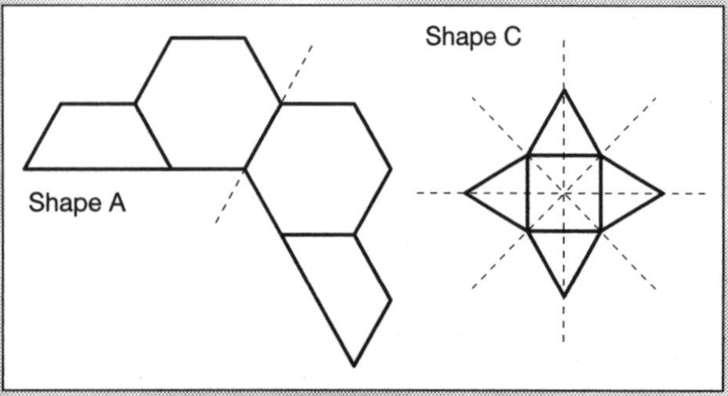

Figure 7: *Lines of symmetry*

Developing the Activity

This activity develops many of the unit's key ideas—working with shapes, discussing their properties, and measuring area and perimeter. These lessons are suitable for students working in pairs if each pair has three triangles.

Part 1. Building with Triangles

Students discuss the properties, area, and perimeter of one triangle. The discussion questions on the *Building with Triangles* Activity Pages in the *Student Guide* introduce or review concepts and vocabulary used in the lesson. For example, *Question 2* defines a **vertex** as a corner of a shape. *Question 3* asks students to identify any right angles in the triangle by comparing each angle to a corner of a square. (If square tangram pieces are not available, students can use a corner of a piece of paper.) *Questions 4* and *5* ask students to measure the area of a triangle to the nearest square inch and the perimeter to the nearest half centimeter. From the drawing, students can see that each triangle measures one square inch and use a ruler to measure the perimeter.

These pages also introduce the edge-to-edge rule that is used throughout the rest of the unit. By this, we mean that shapes must be built with only edges of the same length touching and with those edges meeting along their entire length. Shapes with triangles that overlap or touch only at one point are not used in this activity. This rule limits the number of figures that can be made and facilitates record keeping.

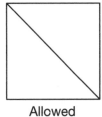

Figure 8: *Edge-to-edge rule*

Allowed   Not Allowed

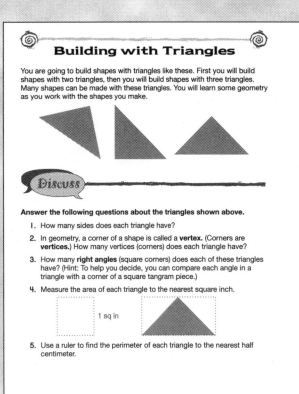

Building with Triangles

You are going to build shapes with triangles like these. First you will build shapes with two triangles, then you will build shapes with three triangles. Many shapes can be made with these triangles. You will learn some geometry as you work with the shapes you make.

Discuss

Answer the following questions about the triangles shown above.

1. How many sides does each triangle have?
2. In geometry, a corner of a shape is called a **vertex**. (Corners are **vertices.**) How many vertices (corners) does each triangle have?
3. How many **right angles** (square corners) does each of these triangles have? (Hint: To help you decide, you can compare each angle in a triangle with a corner of a square tangram piece.)
4. Measure the area of each triangle to the nearest square inch.

   1 sq in

5. Use a ruler to find the perimeter of each triangle to the nearest half centimeter.

Student Guide - Page 166

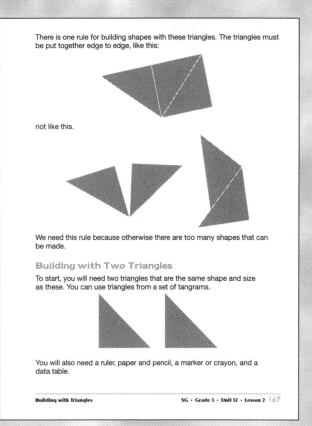

There is one rule for building shapes with these triangles. The triangles must be put together edge to edge, like this:

not like this.

We need this rule because otherwise there are too many shapes that can be made.

Building with Two Triangles

To start, you will need two triangles that are the same shape and size as these. You can use triangles from a set of tangrams.

You will also need a ruler, paper and pencil, a marker or crayon, and a data table.

Student Guide - Page 167

Student Guide Page 168 (boxed)

Find all the different shapes you can by putting two triangles together edge to edge. Count two shapes as the same if they are congruent.

Two shapes are **congruent** if they have the same size and shape. You can show that one shape is congruent to another by moving it so that it covers the other shape exactly. You may need to flip it.

Cover one shape below using two triangles. Show that it is congruent to the second shape by moving it to cover the second shape.

6. Using two triangles, draw all the shapes you find on a sheet of paper. Place dots at the corners and connect the dots with a ruler. Be sure you follow the edge-to-edge rule.

7. Outline the outside border of each shape with a marker or crayon.

8. When you have found all the shapes that can be made with two triangles and have drawn them on a sheet of paper, complete the following for each shape: (Put your answers in a table. Follow the example in the first row of the table.)

   A. Give a name to each shape. Write the name in the first column.

   B. Make a sketch of each shape in the second column of the table.

   C. Count the sides of each shape.

   D. Count the corners (vertices).

   E. Count the right angles inside the shape.

This shape has 3 sides and 1 right angle.

168 SG · Grade 3 · Unit 12 · Lesson 2   **Building with Triangles**

Student Guide - Page 168

Content Note (boxed)

Two Parallelograms? Students are likely to make the following parallelograms.

To show these are congruent you must use a flip.

Part 2. Building with Two Triangles

In this section, students make all possible shapes using two of their triangles. They keep a record of their shapes and analyze them. Figure 9 shows the only three shapes that can be made and names that students have given them.

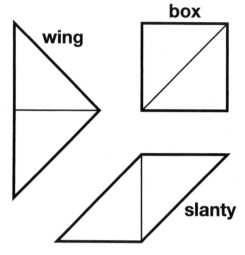

Figure 9: *Shapes made with two isosceles right triangles*

The *Building with Triangles* Activity Pages also state a second rule: Turns and flips of a given shape (congruent figures) are considered to be the same shape. You might also discuss the fact that we could consider turns and flips to be different if we wished—in some contexts, turned and flipped shapes may not be equivalent.

You can use the *When Are Shapes the Same?* Transparency Master to demonstrate turns, flips, and congruence. Place the transparency on the overhead projector and ask students if the two shapes are congruent. Remind them that the shapes are **congruent** if you can turn or flip one so that it exactly covers the other. Encourage students to make copies of shapes to help them decide congruence. After some discussion, cut the transparency along the dotted line and show students that the lower figure can be turned and flipped so that it exactly covers the upper figure. Use other figures as needed to explore congruence. Take two sheets of acetate to make two copies of a shape. One copy can be turned or flipped to check congruence.

As students find shapes they can make with two triangles, you might ask them to draw them on the chalkboard. This will provide good material for a discussion of same and different. You will probably find that these chalkboard drawings are not particularly accurate—angles, in particular, are likely to be distorted. Their drawings can motivate a discussion of the relative sizes of the parts of triangles. We do not recommend that you refer to the triangles as "isosceles right triangles with a 2-inch hypotenuse," but you will want students to notice that two angles are equal, that the other angle is a right angle (square corner), that two sides are equal, and that the third side is longer.

Naming the shapes will make talking about them easier. Ask students to propose names for the shapes as they are drawn on the chalkboard. Standard mathematical terminology is not necessary in this lesson, since the concept of a mathematical definition is better dealt with in later grades. For example, calling the shapes in Figure 9 triangle, square, and parallelogram may reinforce the incorrect notion that a square is not a parallelogram. Calling the shapes "wing," "box," and "slanty," for example, avoids this danger. These issues are explored further in the Professor Peabody's Shape Riddles section of Lesson 3 *Building with Four Triangles.*

After students have found their shapes, *Questions 6* and *7* tell them to record each shape on paper and to outline the outside border using a marker or crayon. This will facilitate counting the sides and corners. Next, students analyze their shapes. *Question 8* gives directions for recording information about each shape on the *Building with Triangles Data Table 1* Activity Page in the *Discovery Assignment Book.*

📓 Journal Prompt

Ask students to write how they know they have found all possible shapes that can be made with two triangles put together edge to edge. You might tell them that "Mr. I.B. Dense" thinks he has a shape that is different from those in Figure 9 and ask them to write a letter to him explaining why he must be wrong.

Content Note

Same and Different: Flips, Turns, and Congruence. The three shapes in Figure 9 are all that can be made if turns and flips are not counted as different. This rule follows common mathematical convention: Shapes that are congruent are usually understood to be "the same." This rule also conveniently limits the number of different shapes that are possible, but it may also confuse some students. Although the shape in Figure 10 is a square, many students would say that it is a diamond and not a square because it is turned from the standard position.

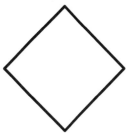

Figure 10: *Is this figure a square?*

Name _____ Date _____

Building with Triangles Data Table 1

Number of triangles used _____ Partner(s) _____

Name of Shape	Sketch	No. of Sides	No. of Corners (vertices)	No. of Right Angles	Area (sq in)	Perimeter (cm)

Building with Triangles   DAB · Grade 3 · Unit 12 · Lesson 2 187

Discovery Assignment Book - Page 187

Counting sides and corners *(Questions 8C* and *8D)* is not too difficult although some students may be distracted by the interior triangles. They may, for example, claim that the shape on the left in Figure 11 has four sides. In a sense, this is correct, but this is not the sense we mean. Only the outline is to be considered. Drawings like the one on the right in Figure 11 may be easier to analyze.

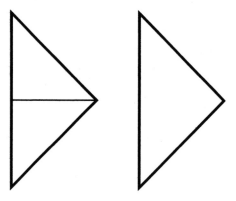

Figure 11: *A shape with interior triangles shown and not shown*

Counting right angles is tricky *(Question 8E)*. Most students have difficulty understanding what a right angle is. Even if they do, right angles can be hard to pick out among the visual clutter of the interior triangles. Using the corner of a square or a piece of paper or a book (as in *Question 3*) is one way to check if an angle is right or not. Using outline shapes (with interior triangles suppressed as shown in Figure 11) may also help. Items B and D in the Daily Practice and Problems familiarize students with right angles and should be completed before students try to count right angles in their shapes.

Questions 8F and *8G* ask students to record the area and perimeter of each shape. Note that finding the area should be straightforward since each triangle measures approximately one square inch. Students need only count the number of triangles in each figure. Students may need to review perimeter, a concept that was introduced in *Walking around Shapes* in Unit 7 *Multiplication and Division*. One way to find the perimeter is to measure the length of each side with a ruler and then to add those lengths; another way is to begin measuring each side at the spot on the ruler where the previous side ended. Inches or centimeters can be used to measure— either way, the answers will not come out even. However, since centimeters are smaller (hence, more accurate) and also yield fractions that are more manageable, we recommend that students measure the perimeter to the nearest half centimeter.

F. Find the area of each shape. (Hint: The area of each small triangle is 1 square inch.)

G. Use a ruler to measure the perimeter of each shape to the nearest half centimeter.

Name of Shape	Sketch	No. of Sides	No. of Corners (vertices)	No. of Right Angles	Area (sq in)	Perimeter (cm)
wing		3	3	1	2	17

9. A. Which of your shapes have line symmetry? (If a shape has **line symmetry,** you can fold the shape in half and the halves will match exactly.)

   B. Draw lines of symmetry on your sketches in the second column of your data table. Follow the example.

10. Find and describe at least one pattern in your table.

Building with Three Triangles

11. Now, find all the shapes that can be made by putting three triangles together edge to edge. Use three triangles like these.

Analyze each of the shapes using Questions 8 and 9 as a guide. Write your answers in a table like the one you used in your work with two triangles.

12. Find and describe a pattern in your new table.

Building with Triangles   SG · Grade 3 · Unit 12 · Lesson 2   169

Student Guide - Page 169

TIMS Tip

To help students recall what perimeter is, you might introduce a bug named Perry Meter. Perry walks completely around the outside of a plane figure and when he reaches his starting point, he reports the distance he has traveled. For convenience, Perry should start at a corner, but this is not strictly necessary.

A relationship exists between the number of sides and the number of corners of these shapes: They are equal. This is one of the patterns we expect students to find when they have completed their data tables *(Question 10)*.

Part 3. Building with Three Triangles

Question 11 asks students to repeat the basic steps in *Questions 6–10* using three triangles in their data collection. Figure 12 shows the four shapes that can be made with three triangles and names students have given them. If your students did well with the two-triangle case, consider using the Building with Three Triangles section as homework.

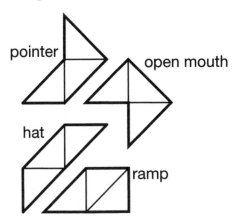

Figure 12: *Shapes from three isosceles right triangles put together edge to edge*

The three-triangle case is not much different from the two-triangle case. One new wrinkle is that one of the shapes can be dissected in two different ways. Figure 13 shows the shape and both dissections. For simplicity, we want to consider these shapes to be the same, just as we consider flips and turns to be the same. Your students may not raise this point, and we recommend that it is best not to bring it up if it is not mentioned. The important thing to stress is different outline shapes; the interior triangles do not matter.

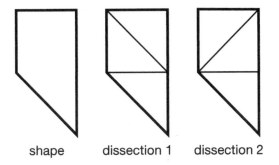

shape   dissection 1   dissection 2

Figure 13: *Alternate dissections of a shape*

Content Note

Proof. In his wonderful book *How to Solve It,* George Polya distinguished problems to find and problems to prove. Most problems children encounter are problems that require an answer to be found, usually through computation; these are "problems to find." Making a mathematical argument—like showing that no shapes can be made with two triangles other than those in Figure 9—is a "problem to prove." You may find the arguments your students give are inadequate at first, but they will improve with practice. Spend some extra time discussing your students' arguments in order to clarify what makes them compelling or not compelling.

Daily Practice and Problems: Task for Lesson 2

F. Task: Tricky Change
(URG p. 12)

Sally has a pocket of pennies, dimes, and quarters. She reaches in and pulls out four coins.

1. What amount of money might Sally have? List three different amounts.

2. What is the least she could have?

3. What is the most?

4. Could she have pulled out 12 cents? 8 cents? 25 cents? 46 cents?

Name_____ Date _____

Building with Triangles Data Table 2

Number of triangles used _____ Partner(s) _____

Name of Shape	Sketch	No. of Sides	No. of Corners (vertices)	No. of Right Angles	Area (sq in)	Perimeter (cm)

Copyright © Kendall/Hunt Publishing Company

Discovery Assignment Book - Page 188

Suggestions for Teaching the Lesson

Homework and Practice

- DPP Bit E provides two word problems using multiplication. DPP Task F is a word problem involving money.

- The section Building with Three Triangles is appropriate for homework after students have completed Building with Two Triangles. Note that students will need triangles, rulers, and the *Building with Triangles Data Table 2* in the *Discovery Assignment Book.*

- Home Practice Part 2 provides further practice with addition and subtraction computation.

Answers for Part 2 of the Home Practice can be found in the Answer Key at the end of this lesson and at the end of this unit.

Assessment

- Assess students' abilities to identify right angles, to recognize if two shapes are congruent, to show line symmetry, and to measure area and perimeter. Record your observations on the *Observational Assessment Record.*

- Use the Journal Prompt to observe how students are using terminology and concepts to explain their reasoning.

Name_____ Date _____

Unit 12: Home Practice

Part 1

Estimate to be sure your answers are reasonable.

| 1. | 285 +300 | 2. | 285 +318 | 3. | 872 −400 | 4. | 872 −490 |

5. Explain your estimation strategy for Question 4.

6. Marie has 748 marbles in her collection. She wants 1000. How many more marbles does she need?

Part 2

| 1. | 115 +27 | 2. | 127 +74 | 3. | 280 −33 | 4. | 325 −76 |

5. Explain a strategy for using mental math for Question 3.

6. Ted read a book for 43 minutes on Saturday and 29 minutes on Sunday.
   A. Did Ted read for more than one hour? Explain how you know.

   B. How many minutes did Ted read? _____

Copyright © Kendall/Hunt Publishing Company

Discovery Assignment Book - Page 178

AT A GLANCE

Math Facts and Daily Practice and Problems

DPP items E and F are word problems.

Part 1. Building with Triangles

1. Students answer *Questions 1–5* in the *Student Guide* that introduce and review vocabulary students will use to analyze shapes.
2. Introduce the edge-to-edge rule.

Part 2. Building with Two Triangles

1. Use the *When Are Shapes the Same?* Transparency Master to define congruent shapes and discuss "same" and "different."
2. Students make shapes using two triangles, draw them on paper, and outline the outside border in markers or crayons. *(Questions 6–7)*
3. Students analyze the shapes using *Question 8* and record their findings on the *Building with Triangles Data Table 1* Activity Page in the *Discovery Assignment Book*.
4. Students identify those shapes with line symmetry and draw the lines of symmetry on the sketches of the shapes in their data tables. *(Question 9)*
5. For *Question 10,* students describe patterns they find in their data tables.

Part 3. Building with Three Triangles

For *Questions 11–12,* students build shapes with three triangles, analyze the shapes, and record their findings on the *Building with Triangles Data Table 2*.

Homework

1. Assign the Building with Three Triangles section for homework.
2. Assign Home Practice Part 2.

Assessment

1. During the activity observe students' abilities to identify right angles, recognize congruent shapes, show lines of symmetry, and measure area and perimeter. Record your observations on the *Observational Assessment Record*.
2. Use the Journal Prompt to assess students' abilities to explain their reasoning.

Notes:

Lines of Symmetry

1. Cut out the shapes.

2. Fold the shapes to see if they have a line of symmetry.

3. Draw the lines of symmetry on each shape.

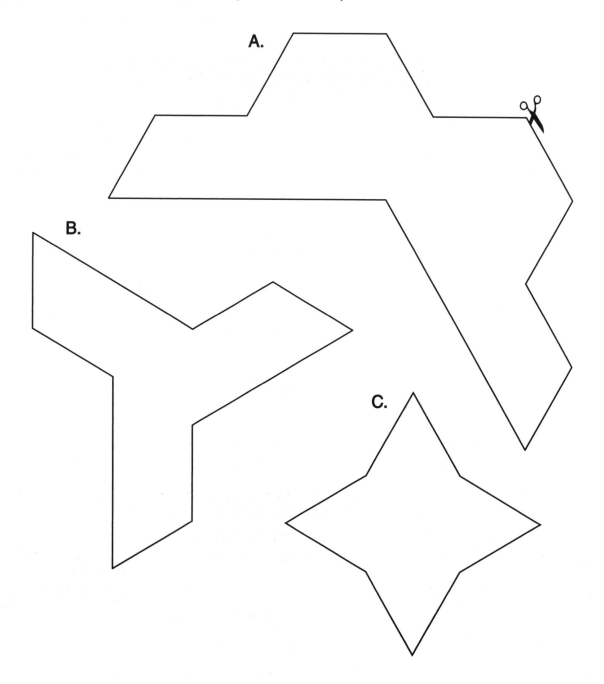

Name _____ Date _____

Right Triangle Master

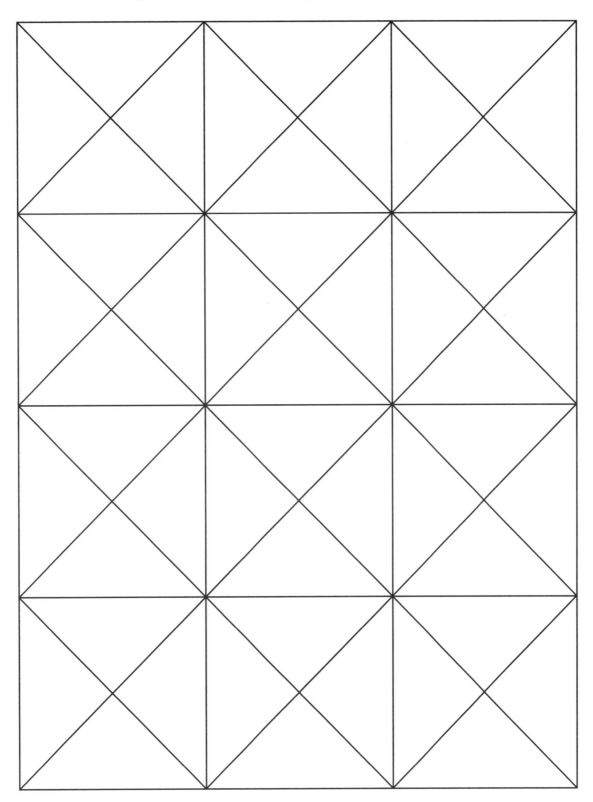

When Are Shapes the Same?

Are these two figures congruent?

Transparency Master

Student Guide

Questions 1–12 (SG pp. 166–169)

1. 3 sides

2. 3 corners or vertices

3. 1 square corner or right angle

4. 1 sq in

5. 12 cm

6–8. **A.** Names for these shapes will vary.

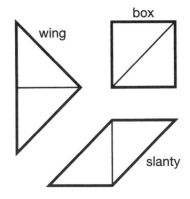

8. **A–G.**

Name	# Sides	# Corners	# right angle	Area (sq in)	Perimeter (cm)
wing	3	3	1	2 sq in	17 cm
box	4	4	4	2 sq in	14 cm
slanty	4	4	0	2 sq in	17 cm

9. **A.** wing and box

B.

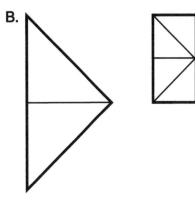

10. Answers will vary. The area of all three shapes is 2 sq in. The perimeter of two of the types is the same—17 cm. The perimeters of wing and slanty are made up of the same sides—2 short sides (the legs of the right triangles) and 2 long sides (the hypotenuse). The number of sides always equals the number of corners.

11. The names of the shapes will vary. Note: Only the interior angles were counted for 90° angles. Your students may choose to count both.

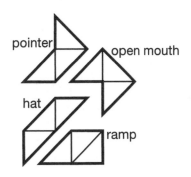

Name	# Sides	# Corners	# right angle	Area (sq in)	Perimeter (cm)
pointer	5	5	1	3 sq in	22 cm
open mouth	5	5	2	3 sq in	22 cm
hat	4	4	0	3 sq in	22 cm
ramp	4	4	2	3 sq in	19 cm

*Answers and/or discussion are included in the Lesson Guide.

**Answers for all the Home Practice in the *Discovery Assignment Book* are at the end of the unit.

12. Answers will vary. The number of corners equals the number of sides. The area of all four shapes is the same—3 sq in. The perimeter of three of the shapes is the same—22 cm.

Discovery Assignment Book

**Home Practice (DAB p. 178)

Part 2

Questions 1–6

1. 142

2. 201

3. 247

4. 249

5. Possible strategy $280 - 30 = 250$ and $250 - 3 = 247$.

6. **A.** Yes; $40 + 20 = 60$; 43 and 29 are greater than 40 and 20

   B. 72 minutes or 1 hour and 12 minutes

Unit Resource Guide

Lines of Symmetry (URG p. 42)

Questions A–C

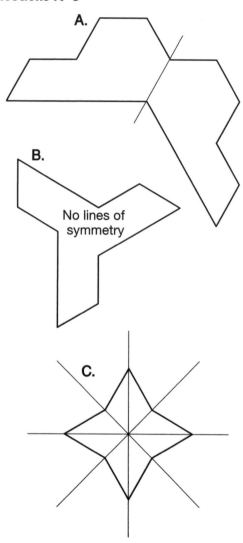

A.

B.

No lines of symmetry

C.

*Answers and/or discussion are included in the Lesson Guide.

**Answers for all the Home Practice in the *Discovery Assignment Book* are at the end of the unit.

46　　URG • Grade 3 • Unit 12 • Lesson 2 • Answer Key

LESSON GUIDE 3

Building with Four Triangles

Estimated Class Sessions: 2

This activity continues and extends the previous activity, *Building with Triangles.* Shapes that can be made with four isosceles right triangles put together edge to edge are investigated.

Key Content

- Representing shapes using manipulatives, drawings, and words.
- Using flips and turns to identify shapes that are congruent.
- Analyzing and classifying shapes using their properties (number of sides, corners, right angles, and lines of symmetry).
- Measuring area and perimeter.

Key Vocabulary

congruent
corner (vertex)
hexagon
line of symmetry
pentagon
quadrilateral

Daily Practice and Problems: Bits for Lesson 3

G. Subtraction (URG p. 13)

Complete the following problems. Use pencil and paper or mental math to find the answers.

1.	594 − 225	2.	6784 − 2387
3.	231 − 179	4.	602 − 199

Explain your strategy for Question 3.

I. Bus Stop (URG p. 14)

Starting at 7:00 in the morning, a bus passes Ellen's stop every 15 minutes.

1. How many minutes must Ellen wait for the next bus if she gets to the stop at 9:05?

2. Will a bus come at 4:20 in the afternoon? How do you know?

DPP Tasks are on page 52. Suggestions for using the DPPs are on page 52.

Materials List

Print Materials for Students

	Math Facts and Daily Practice and Problems	Activity	Homework	Written Assessment
Student Books — Student Guide		*Building with Four Triangles* Pages 170–172		
Student Books — Discovery Assignment Book			Home Practice Part 3 Page 179	
Teacher Resources — Facts Resource Guide	DPP Item 12J			
Teacher Resources — Unit Resource Guide	DPP Items G–J Pages 13–14	*Four Triangles Data Tables 1* and *2* Pages 54–55, and *Tangram Pieces Master* Page 27, 1 each per student group (optional)		*Three Tans,* Pages 56–57, 1 per student

⊙ *available on Teacher Resource CD*

All Transparency Masters, Blackline Masters, and Assessment Blackline Masters in the Unit Resource Guide are on the Teacher Resource CD.

Supplies for Each Student

scissors
centimeter ruler
plain paper (to sketch shapes)

Supplies for Each Student Group

envelope (for storing cutout shapes)
2 sets of tangrams per group

Materials for the Teacher

Transparency of *Four Triangles Data Tables 1* and *2* Blackline Masters (Unit Resource Guide) Pages 54–55
Transparency of *Tangram Pieces Master* Blackline Master (Unit Resource Guide), Page 27 (color and cut) or
2 sets of tangram pieces

Before the Activity

The rules and procedures in this lesson follow the working pattern established in Lesson 2 *Building with Triangles*. Please refer to that lesson for the necessary background. Each group will need four of the smallest tangram triangles and one square tangram. Provide each group with one copy of the *Tangram Pieces Master* Blackline Master or two sets of tangram pieces. If actual tangram pieces are used, they should be close to the same size as those on the *Tangram Pieces Master*.

Developing the Activity

This lesson includes an extended investigation of shapes that can be made with four isosceles right triangles and a similar assessment exercise. Most of the activities are suitable for groups of two or three students working together.

The first page of the *Building with Four Triangles* Activity Pages describes in words some shapes for students to make using four triangles. With four triangles, there are many shapes that can be made. The first three shapes to be made—square, nonsquare rectangle, and triangle—have unique solutions, except for variations in the placement of the interior triangles. The next three shapes—nonrectangular quadrilateral, pentagon, and hexagon—have multiple nonequivalent solutions. Figure 14 shows the fourteen shapes that we have found.

Figure 14: *Fourteen ways of putting four isosceles right triangles together edge to edge*

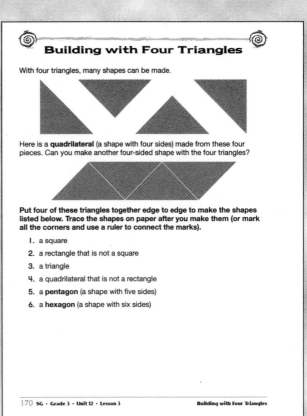

Student Guide - Page 170

Student Guide - Page 171

Professor Peabody's Shapes

Professor Peabody made shapes with four triangles put together edge to edge. He used four triangles like this one.

He named his shapes and sketched the outlines, but he forgot to show the inner lines for each triangle.

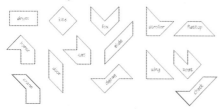

7. Use four triangles to make some of Professor Peabody's shapes. Your teacher will tell you which shapes your group will make and measure. Draw the shapes on paper. Show where the inner triangles go.

8. Count the sides, corners, and right angles for each of the shapes your group is working on. Write this information down next to each shape so you can share it with your classmates.

9. Measure and record the area and perimeter of each shape. Find the perimeter to the nearest half centimeter with your ruler.

Remember we discovered that the area of one small triangle is one square inch.

Building with Four Triangles   SG · Grade 3 · Unit 12 · Lesson 3   171

Student Guide - Page 172

Be ready to record your measurements in a data table like this one so you can share your data with the class.

Name of Shape	Sketch	No. of Sides	No. of Corners (vertices)	No. of Right Angles	Area (sq in)	Perimeter (cm)

10. Which of Professor Peabody's shapes have line symmetry? Draw the lines of symmetry on your sketches and in the data table.

11. Find and describe a pattern in your data. Explain why the pattern happens.

Professor Peabody's Shape Riddles

Solve Professor Peabody's riddles about his four-triangle shapes.

12. We are the only shapes with 5 sides (pentagons). Who are we?

13. I have the most right angles and the smallest perimeter. Who am I?

14. I have the fewest right angles and the largest perimeter. Who am I?

15. I am a hexagon. If you turn me halfway around, then I look the same. Who am I?

16. I have four lines of symmetry. Who am I?

17. Make up a riddle of your own. The answer to your riddle should be one or more of Professor Peabody's shapes. Use clues about symmetry, area, perimeter, number of sides, and so on. Write your riddle neatly, and write the answer in another place. Trade with a friend and solve each other's riddles. Fix your riddle if it has a mistake.

172 SG · Grade 3 · Unit 12 · Lesson 3   Building with Four Triangles

---

This profusion of four-triangle shapes allows plenty of room for open-ended work. We encourage you to let your students try to find as many of the fourteen possible shapes as they can.

At the same time, however, this abundance of shapes makes it difficult to organize the investigation, to have a coherent discussion, and to achieve closure. In the section Professor Peabody's Shapes, Professor Peabody comes to the rescue. Peabody has found and named all fourteen shapes, but he has failed to draw in the interior triangles. With this hint, students can track down any shapes they haven't already made.

> **TIMS Tip**
>
> Instead of filling out a data table for their shapes, students may record all measurements (using units) for each shape neatly next to their tracings of the shapes. Then, students may transfer their data to the transparencies of *Four Triangles Data Table 1* and *2*.

To investigate each of Professor Peabody's shapes, students repeat the same type of inquiries they carried out for shapes in Lesson 2. They count the number of sides, corners, and interior right angles. They also measure area and perimeter.

This task is particularly appropriate for groups of two or three students. So that each group does not have to make measurements for all fourteen shapes, assign only a few shapes to each group. Provide each group with a copy of either *Four Triangles Data Table 1* or *2,* and mark the shapes you expect each group to investigate. Students must make and trace each of their shapes on their own paper so they can make all measurements accurately. Student groups record their measurements on their copy of the data table, then transfer their data onto a transparency of the data table. Once all the data has been collected and recorded, discuss any patterns students see.

The next section, Professor Peabody's Shape Riddles, provides five riddles for students to solve. Then, students compose their own. Solving these riddles requires logical thinking and classification by multiple variables. You can begin by working through one or two riddles as a class and then send the rest home. Put your students in small groups, pose a riddle, give students a few minutes to work, then ask students to share their results and their reasoning. Use the Professor Peabody's riddles or make up your own. Here are two other riddles you might ask:

- We are the only shapes with no right angle. Who are we? (slide, door, flattop)
- We have exactly one line of symmetry. Who are we? (cat, fox, wing, flattop)

▤ Journal Prompt

Imagine that you are writing a riddle about Professor Peabody's shapes for homework, but you have forgotten your *Student Guide*. You can't remember the name of your shape. Draw your shape in your journal. Then, write what you would say on the telephone to a friend so that your friend could look up the shape and tell you its name.

Daily Practice and Problems:
Tasks for Lesson 3

H. Task: Larry the Lizard Show

(URG p. 13)

Use the Lizardland picture in the *Student Guide* in Unit 11 to solve the following problems. 178 people attended the 10 A.M. show. 284 people attended the noon show.

1. How many more people attended the noon show than the 10 A.M. show?

2. How many people attended the first two shows?

3. How many empty seats were there during the first two shows?

J. Task: Story Solving

(URG p. 14)

1. $3 \times 9 = ?$ Write a story and draw a picture about 3×9. Write a number sentence on your picture.

2. $3 \times \frac{1}{2} = ?$ Write a story, and draw a picture about $3 \times \frac{1}{2}$. Write a number sentence on your picture.

Name _____ Date _____

Part 3

Girl Scout Troop 903 went to Lizardland. Thirty-five girls were accompanied by seven adults. Use this information to solve the following problems:

1. The Girl Scout troop is standing in line for the Leaping Lizard roller coaster. There are 8 cars on the roller coaster and each car can hold 4 people. Can the entire group ride the roller coaster at one time? Explain.

2. If 8 people can ride the Lizard-Go-Round at the same time, how many rides will it take for all the girls to ride one time? Explain.

3. The troop is standing in line for the Bump-a-Lizard bumper cars. Each car holds 2 people. How many bumper cars will the troop need for everyone in the group? Explain.

4. The Curly-Whirly-Lizard ride fits 3 people per car. There are 15 cars on the ride.
   A. Can the entire group ride the ride at the same time? Explain.
   B. If one adult rode in a car of girls, how many cars would not have an adult?

Part 4

1. Look at the six shapes below. Draw an **X** on the right angle(s) inside the shapes.

2. If any of the six shapes are symmetrical, draw in the lines of symmetry that divide the shape in half.

DISSECTIONS   DAB · Grade 3 · Unit 12 179

Discovery Assignment Book - Page 179

Suggestions for Teaching the Lesson

Math Facts

Task J develops strategies for multiplying by three.

Homework and Practice

- DPP Bit G and Task H are problems involving subtraction. Task I is a problem involving bus times.

- The Professor Peabody's Shape Riddles section is appropriate for homework. Pose and discuss several riddles in class before sending this work home. Students will need to take their *Student Guide,* four triangles, and sketches home.

- Home Practice Part 3 provides practice with multiplication and division.

Answers for Part 3 of the Home Practice can be found in the Answer Key at the end of this lesson and at the end of this unit.

Assessment

On the *Three Tans* Assessment Pages, students cover each of four shapes with three given tans. Students will need the three shapes and a centimeter ruler. After students identify which shapes can be covered with the three tangram pieces, they then count the sides, corners, right angles, and measure the area and perimeter of those shapes. Students record the measurements in a data table. Shapes 1 and 4 can be covered. Students should trace the three tangram pieces on these two shapes to show where each piece needs to be placed to fill the outline exactly. Shapes 2 and 3 cannot be covered. Ask students to explain why they are impossible to solve. The challenge question asks students to use three tangram pieces to find as many shapes as can be made. Students may record these shapes on a separate sheet of paper by tracing each shape they find.

AT A GLANCE

Math Facts and Daily Practice and Problems

DPP items G and H are problems involving subtraction. Item I is a problem involving time. For item J, students illustrate multiplication number sentences.

Developing the Activity

1. Students complete *Questions 1–6* on the *Building with Four Triangles* Activity Page. They create and trace shapes using four triangle tangram pieces.

2. Student groups are assigned some of the fourteen shapes shown in the Professor Peabody's Shapes section. They make and trace the shapes using four triangle tangram pieces and draw lines to show where the inner triangles go. *(Question 7)*

3. Students fill in the appropriate rows of *Four Triangles Data Table 1* or *2* after measuring the assigned shapes. *(Questions 8–10)*

4. Students transfer their data onto the class transparency of the data tables.

5. The class discusses any patterns found in the data shown on the overhead. *(Question 11)*

6. Students solve a few riddles in the Professor Peabody's Shapes Riddles section. Assign the rest for homework. *(Questions 12–16)*

7. Students make up their own riddles to share with classmates. *(Question 17)*

Homework

1. Assign some of Professor Peabody's Shape Riddles.
2. Assign Home Practice Part 3.

Assessment

Students complete the *Three Tans* Assessment Pages.

Notes:

Four Triangles Data Table 1

Name of Shape	Sketch	No. of Sides	No. of Corners (vertices)	No. of Right Angles	Area (sq in)	Perimeter (cm)
drum						
kite						
fox						
stroller						
flattop						
horse						
door						

Four Triangles Data Table 2

Name of Shape	Sketch	No. of Sides	No. of Corners (vertices)	No. of Right Angles	Area (sq in)	Perimeter (cm)
cat						
slide						
zigzag						
wing						
boat						
crane						
check						

Three Tans

1. Use the three tangram pieces that match those above to cover the shapes below.

2. If a shape can be covered exactly, draw lines inside it to show how.

3. Complete the data table for only those shapes below that can be covered.

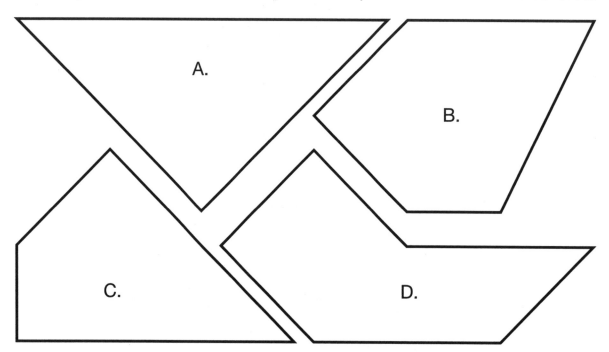

Name _____   Date _____

Number of Shape	Sketch	No. of Sides	No. of Corners (vertices)	No. of Right Angles	Area (sq in)	Perimeter (cm)

4. If a shape cannot be covered, explain why in a sentence or two.

Challenge: Find all of the shapes that can be made by putting these three tans together edge to edge. Draw the shapes on a separate sheet of paper.

Student Guide

Questions 1–17 (SG pp. 170–172)

The names of the shapes refer to the names Professor Peabody uses in the *Student Guide*.

1.  kite

2.  drum

3. wing

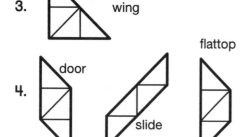

4. door, flattop, slide

5. 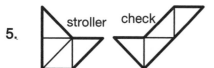 stroller, check

6. 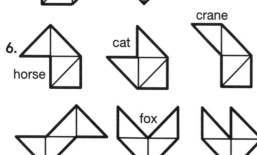 horse, cat, crane, zigzag, fox, boat

7. See the shapes shown for *Questions 1–6* for one way to fill in each shape.

8–9. The names in the table refer to the names Professor Peabody uses.

Name	# Sides	# Corners	# right angle	Area (sq in)	Perimeter (cm)
drum	4	4	4	4 sq in	21 cm
kite	4	4	4	4 sq in	20 cm
fox	6	6	1	4 sq in	27 cm
stroller	5	5	1	4 sq in	24 cm
flat-top	4	4	0	4 sq in	24 cm
horse	6	6	3	4 sq in	24 cm
door	4	4	0	4 sq in	24 cm
cat	6	6	1	4 sq in	24 cm
slide	4	4	0	4 sq in	27 cm
zigzag	6	6	2	4 sq in	27 cm
wing	3	3	1	4 sq in	24 cm
boat	6	6	2	4 sq in	27 cm
crane	6	6	2	4 sq in	24 cm
check	5	5	1	4 sq in	27 cm

*Answers and/or discussion are included in the Lesson Guide.

**Answers for all the Home Practice in the *Discovery Assignment Book* are at the end of the unit.

10.

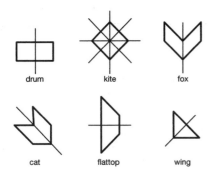

drum   kite   fox

cat   flattop   wing

11. The number of corners and the number of sides are always equal. The area is always 4 sq inches because each shape is made up of 4 triangles that are each 1 sq inch. Although there are 14 different shapes there are only 4 different measurements for the perimeter. Explanations will vary.

12. check and stroller

13. kite

14. slide

15. zigzag

16. kite

17. Riddles will vary.

Discovery Assignment Book

**Home Practice (DAB p. 179)

Part 3

Questions 1–4

1. No, there are 42 people in the troop and the roller coaster can only hold 32 people.

2. 5 rides. 32 girls can ride in 4 rides but there are 3 girls left. Therefore it will take one more ride for all the girls to ride.

3. 21 bumper cars. 42 people in the group divide into 21 groups of 2.

4. A. Yes, the ride holds 45 people and there are 42 people in the group.

   B. 7 cars; 14 girls will ride with seven adults leaving 21 girls to ride without an adult. 21 is seven groups of three.

Unit Resource Guide

Three Tans (URG pp. 56–57)

1–4.

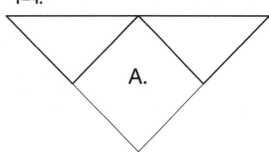

A.

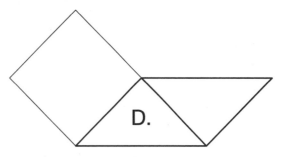

D.

3.

Name	# Sides	# Corners	# right angle	Area sq in	Perimeter cm
A wing	3	3	1	4 sq in	24 cm
D shoe	6	6	2	4 sq in	24 cm

4. The area of shape B is correct (a fact that may escape some students), but the angles are wrong. In particular, the angle at the top right corner cannot be matched by any combination of the three given tans (or any other combination of tangram pieces). A good student response addresses these points, preferably using terms like area and angles. The area of shape C is incorrect. This shape has an area of 3.5 sq in; the three tans have a total area of 4 sq in. Hence this shape cannot be covered exactly without overlapping the three tans.

---

*Answers and/or discussion are included in the Lesson Guide.

**Answers for all the Home Practice in the *Discovery Assignment Book* are at the end of the unit.

Challenge:

This problem requires a systematic search. To see that the following shapes are all that can be made, note first that the square and the first triangle can be joined in only one way. There are then five edges where the second triangle can be added. On four of these edges, the second triangle can be joined in two ways. Eliminating shapes obtained in more than one way yields the eight shapes below.

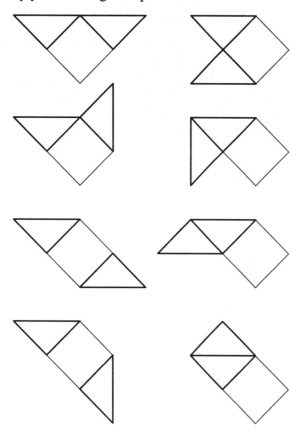

*Answers and/or discussion are included in the Lesson Guide.

**Answers for all the Home Practice in the *Discovery Assignment Book* are at the end of the unit.

LESSON GUIDE

Dissection Puzzles

Estimated Class Sessions: 1

Students solve puzzles that require dissecting figures in specific ways. In each puzzle, they are given a set of pieces that they put together edge to edge to make various shapes. Three such puzzles are included for use now; similar puzzles will appear in the Daily Practice and Problems.

Key Content

- Representing shapes with manipulatives, drawings, and words.
- Developing spatial visualization skills.
- Using geometric concepts and skills.

Daily Practice and Problems: Bit for Lesson 4

K. Using Threes (URG p. 14)

Do these problems in your head. Write only the answers.

A. $3 \times 5 =$ B. $7 \times 3 =$

C. $9 \times 3 =$ D. $3 \times 2 =$

E. $10 \times 3 =$ F. $3 \times 6 =$

G. $4 \times 3 =$ H. $3 \times 3 =$

I. $3 \times 1 =$ J. $8 \times 3 =$

Describe a strategy for 8×3.

DPP Task is on page 64. Suggestions for using the DPPs are on page 64.

Materials List

Print Materials for Students

	Math Facts and Daily Practice and Problems	Activity	Homework
Student Books Student Guide		*Dissection Puzzles* Pages 173–175	
Discovery Assignment Book		*Puzzle Pieces* Page 189	Home Practice Part 4 Page 179
Teacher Resources Facts Resource Guide ⊙	DPP Item 12K		
Unit Resource Guide	DPP Items K–L Pages 14–15 ⊙		

⊙ *available on Teacher Resource CD*

All Transparency Masters, Blackline Masters, and Assessment Blackline Masters in the Unit Resource Guide are on the Teacher Resource CD.

Supplies for Each Student

set of tangram pieces, optional
scissors

Materials for the Teacher

Observational Assessment Record (Unit Resource Guide, Pages 7–8 and Teacher Resource CD)
Individual Assessment Record Sheet (Teacher Implementation Guide, Assessment Section and Teacher Resource CD)

Developing the Activity

These puzzles are variations on the themes that have been explored extensively in Lesson 1 *Tangrams* and Lesson 2 *Building with Triangles*. These puzzles can be used in many ways. All are suitable for homework. The last one (Puzzle C) can be used for assessment.

Students cut out puzzle pieces from the *Puzzle Pieces* Activity Page in the *Discovery Assignment Book*. The three puzzles on the *Dissection Puzzles* Activity Pages in the *Student Guide* prepare students for those they will encounter later in the Daily Practice and Problems.

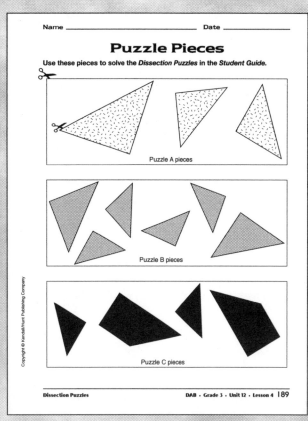

Copyright © Kendall/Hunt Publishing Company

Name _____ Date _____

Puzzle Pieces

Use these pieces to solve the *Dissection Puzzles* in the *Student Guide*.

Puzzle A pieces

Puzzle B pieces

Puzzle C pieces

Dissection Puzzles   DAB · Grade 3 · Unit 12 · Lesson 4 189

Discovery Assignment Book - Page 189

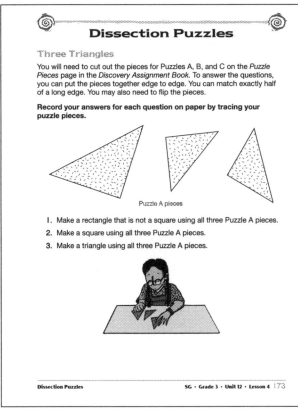

Dissection Puzzles

Three Triangles

You will need to cut out the pieces for Puzzles A, B, and C on the *Puzzle Pieces* page in the *Discovery Assignment Book*. To answer the questions, you can put the pieces together edge to edge. You can match exactly half of a long edge. You may also need to flip the pieces.

Record your answers for each question on paper by tracing your puzzle pieces.

Puzzle A pieces

1. Make a rectangle that is not a square using all three Puzzle A pieces.
2. Make a square using all three Puzzle A pieces.
3. Make a triangle using all three Puzzle A pieces.

Dissection Puzzles   SG · Grade 3 · Unit 12 · Lesson 4 173

Student Guide - Page 173

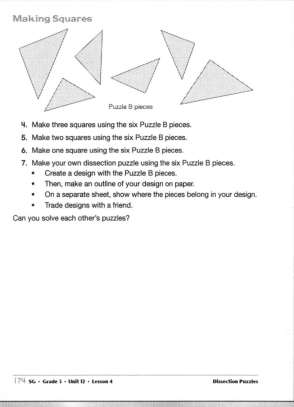

Making Squares

Puzzle B pieces

4. Make three squares using the six Puzzle B pieces.
5. Make two squares using the six Puzzle B pieces.
6. Make one square using the six Puzzle B pieces.
7. Make your own dissection puzzle using the six Puzzle B pieces.
   - Create a design with the Puzzle B pieces.
   - Then, make an outline of your design on paper.
   - On a separate sheet, show where the pieces belong in your design.
   - Trade designs with a friend.

Can you solve each other's puzzles?

174 SG · Grade 3 · Unit 12 · Lesson 4   Dissection Puzzles

Student Guide - Page 174

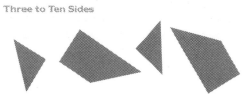

Three to Ten Sides

Puzzle C pieces

8. Make a triangle using all four Puzzle C pieces. Remember to use the edge-to-edge rule.

9. Make a quadrilateral (a shape with four sides) using all four Puzzle C pieces.

10. Make a pentagon (a shape with five sides) using all four Puzzle C pieces.

11. Use the Puzzle C pieces to make shapes with six, seven, eight, nine, and ten sides.

Dissection Puzzles   SG · Grade 3 · Unit 12 · Lesson 4   175

Student Guide - Page 175

Daily Practice and Problems:
Task for Lesson 4

L. Task: Dissection Puzzle 1 (URG p. 15)

Trace and cut out the following triangles.

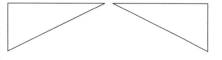

1. Put them edge to edge to make a rectangle.

2. Put them edge to edge to make a triangle.

3. Make four other shapes.

As students try to solve Puzzles A and B, you can provide hints. Tell them that two smaller triangles can be put together edge to edge to form the larger triangle in both puzzle piece sets A and B. Also, remind them that they may flip the pieces if necessary. After students solve the puzzles, they should trace their pieces on paper to show their solutions. Encourage them to share their solutions.

TIMS Tip

Students may use the tangram pieces instead of puzzle pieces A and B. To solve puzzle B, however, two sets of tangram pieces are needed. Four small triangles are needed and two mid-size tangram triangles are needed. If each student is given one set, student pairs can work together to solve Puzzle B. Students must, however, cut out Puzzle C pieces to complete *Questions 8–11.*

Journal Prompt
Ask students to explain how they solved one of these puzzles. They should tell what the puzzle was and what they did to try to solve it.

Suggestions for Teaching the Lesson

Math Facts
DPP Bit K develops strategies for learning the multiplication facts for the threes.

Homework and Practice

- DPP Task L is a dissection puzzle.

- All of the puzzles on the *Dissection Puzzles* Activity Pages are suitable for homework. Students need the *Puzzle Pieces* Activity Page from the *Discovery Assignment Book* to complete the puzzles.

- Home Practice Part 4 provides practice with some of the geometry concepts in this unit.

Answers for Part 4 of the Home Practice can be found in the Answer Key at the end of this lesson and at the end of this unit.

Assessment

These puzzles can provide useful information about students' geometric understanding and communication skills. Puzzle C has both well-defined problems and open-ended investigations, so this one may be more useful for assessment than Puzzles A or B. Use the *Observational Assessment Record* to record students' abilities to analyze and describe two-dimensional shapes and to communicate their reasoning.

Extension

Ask students what other shapes they can make with the Puzzle A pieces after completing *Questions 1–3* in the *Student Guide*. Ask them to make as many shapes as they can. Students can trace their solutions on a piece of paper and share their solutions with the class.

Name _____ Date _____

Part 3

Girl Scout Troop 903 went to Lizardland. Thirty-five girls were accompanied by seven adults. Use this information to solve the following problems:

1. The Girl Scout troop is standing in line for the Leaping Lizard roller coaster. There are 8 cars on the roller coaster and each car can hold 4 people. Can the entire group ride the roller coaster at one time? Explain.

2. If 8 people can ride the Lizard-Go-Round at the same time, how many rides will it take for all the girls to ride one time? Explain.

3. The troop is standing in line for the Bump-a-Lizard bumper cars. Each car holds 2 people. How many bumper cars will the troop need for everyone in the group? Explain.

4. The Curly-Whirly-Lizard ride fits 3 people per car. There are 15 cars on the ride.
   A. Can the entire group ride the ride at the same time? Explain.
   B. If one adult rode in a car of girls, how many cars would not have an adult?

Part 4

1. Look at the six shapes below. Draw an **X** on the right angle(s) inside the shapes.

2. If any of the six shapes are symmetrical, draw in the lines of symmetry that divide the shape in half.

DISSECTIONS   DAB · Grade 3 · Unit 12 179

Discovery Assignment Book - Page 179

AT A GLANCE

Math Facts and Daily Practice and Problems

DPP Bit K provides practice with the multiplication facts for the threes and DPP Task L is a dissection puzzle.

Developing the Activity

1. Students cut out the pieces for Puzzles A, B, and C from the *Puzzle Pieces* Activity Page in the *Discovery Assignment Book.*
2. Students complete the *Dissection Puzzles* Activity Pages in the *Student Guide.* They trace their solutions on paper.
3. Students share their solutions.

Homework

1. Puzzles may be assigned for homework.
2. Assign Home Practice Part 4.

Assessment

1. Puzzle C provides an opportunity to observe students' abilities to analyze and describe two-dimensional shapes. Record your observations on the *Observational Assessment Record.*
2. Transfer information from the Unit 12 *Observational Assessment Record* to students' *Individual Assessment Record Sheet.*

Notes:

Student Guide

Questions 1–11 (SG pp. 173–175)

1.

2.

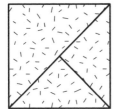

3.

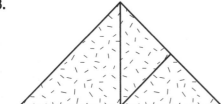

4.

5.

6. Answers will vary. Two solutions are shown below.

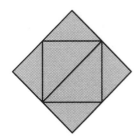 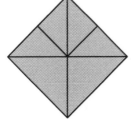

7. Answers will vary.

8. One solution is shown below.

9. Answers will vary. Three solutions are shown below.

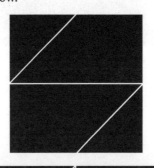

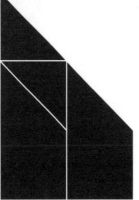

10. Answers will vary.

11. Answers will vary. The following is an example of a shape with seven sides.

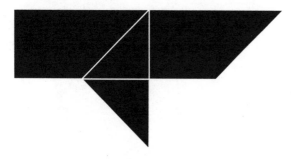

Discovery Assignment Book

**Home Practice (DAB p. 179)

Part 4

Questions 1–2

1–2.

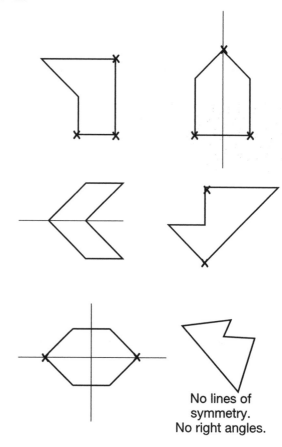

No lines of symmetry. No right angles.

*Answers and/or discussion are included in the Lesson Guide.

**Answers for all the Home Practice in the *Discovery Assignment Book* are at the end of the unit.

Hex

Estimated
Class
Sessions:
1

Students play a geometric game similar to tic-tac-toe or "boxes." In later units, this game will be adapted to provide practice in estimation and mental computation.

Key Content

* Reasoning logically and strategically in a game situation.

Daily Practice and Problems: Bit for Lesson 5

M. Quiz on 2s and 3s (URG p. 15)

A. $4 \times 2 =$	B. $3 \times 2 =$
C. $5 \times 3 =$	D. $2 \times 10 =$
E. $6 \times 3 =$	F. $2 \times 5 =$
G. $10 \times 3 =$	H. $7 \times 2 =$
I. $8 \times 3 =$	J. $3 \times 3 =$
K. $8 \times 2 =$	L. $2 \times 2 =$
M. $9 \times 2 =$	N. $6 \times 2 =$
O. $3 \times 7 =$	P. $4 \times 3 =$
Q. $3 \times 9 =$	R. $3 \times 1 =$

DPP Challenge is on page 71. Suggestions for using the DPPs are on page 71.

Materials List

Print Materials for Students

		Math Facts and Daily Practice and Problems	Game	Written Assessment
Student Book	**Discovery Assignment Book**		*Hex* Page 191	
Teacher Resources	**Facts Resource Guide**	DPP Item 12M		DPP Item 12M *Quiz on 2s and 3s*
	Unit Resource Guide	DPP Items M–N Pages 15–16		DPP Item M *Quiz on 2s and 3s* Page 15

available on Teacher Resource CD

All Transparency Masters, Blackline Masters, and Assessment Blackline Masters in the Unit Resource Guide are on the Teacher Resource CD.

Supplies for Each Student Pair

25 of each of 2 kinds of beans or other small markers

Materials for the Teacher

4-by-4 Hex Transparency Master (Unit Resource Guide) Page 73, optional

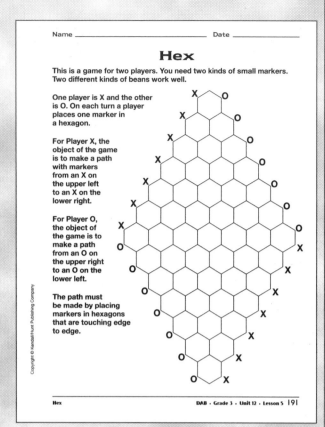

Discovery Assignment Book - Page 191

Developing the Game

As outlined on the *Hex* Game Page in the *Discovery Assignment Book,* players take turns placing one marker on a hexagon. Player X goes first and tries to connect an X on the upper left of the game board to an X on the lower right. Player O tries to connect an O on the upper right of the board to an O on the lower left. Figure 15 shows a game on a smaller board in which Player X went first, using black beans and Player O used white beans.

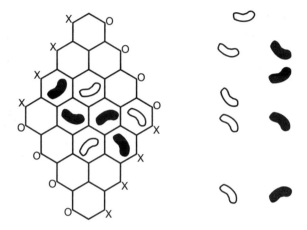

Figure 15: *A win for Player X*

One way to introduce this game is to play against one of your students using a transparency of the *4-by-4 Hex* Transparency Master. The transparency allows for a short game. The regular version has a 7-by-7 array of hexagons.

After the rules are clear, students can play in pairs several times. In later units, variations of this game will involve estimation and mental arithmetic. The game board will be similar but numbers will be located on the hexagons. Students will use estimation to select two numbers that will help them make a path from one side of the game board to the other.

Suggestions for Teaching the Lesson

Homework and Practice

- DPP Challenge N is a dissection puzzle. Encourage students to share their solutions.

- Students can play *Hex* at home with a family member. They will need the *Hex* Game Page in the *Discovery Assignment Book.*

- Assign some or all of the word problems in Lesson 6 *Focus on Word Problems* for homework.

Assessment

DPP Bit M is a quiz on the twos and threes multiplication facts.

Extension

An interesting question is whether the player who goes first, Player X, wins more often than the other player and, if so, why. If Player X always plays first and students tally game outcomes in a data table like the one in Figure 16, then a pattern may emerge.

Player	Wins	
	Tallies	Total
X		
O		

Figure 16: *Table for analyzing whether Player X wins more often*

Daily Practice and Problems:
Challenge for Lesson 5

N. Challenge: Dissection Puzzle 2
   (URG p. 16)

1. Trace and cut out the shapes below.

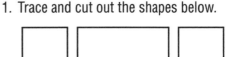

2. Find all shapes that can be made by putting the three pieces edge to edge. Trace them on a piece of paper.

3. Make a data table which shows the area, perimeter, and lines of symmetry for each shape.

AT A GLANCE

Math Facts and Daily Practice and Problems

DPP Bit M is a quiz on the twos and threes multiplication facts. DPP Challenge N is a dissection puzzle.

Developing the Game

1. Introduce the game *Hex* by playing against one student using the *4-by-4 Hex* Transparency Master.
2. Students play the game several times in pairs.

Homework

1. Encourage students to play *Hex* with a family member.
2. Assign the word problems in Lesson 6 for homework.

Assessment

DPP Bit M is a quiz to assess the twos and threes multiplication facts.

Notes:

4-by-4 Hex

OPTIONAL LESSON

There are no Daily Practice and
Problems items for this lesson.

LESSON GUIDE 6

Focus on Word Problems

Estimated
Class
Sessions:
1

Students solve a set of word problems and
share their solutions and strategies.

Key Content

*   Solving multistep word problems.
*   Solving problems involving addition, subtraction,
    multiplication, and division.
*   Choosing to find an estimate or an exact answer.
*   Communicating solutions in writing.

Materials List

Print Materials for Students

		Optional Activity
Student Book	**Student Guide**	*Focus on Word Problems* Pages 176–177
Teacher Resource	**Generic Section** ⊙	*Centimeter Graph Paper,* one per student

⊙ *available on Teacher Resource CD*

*All Transparency Masters, Blackline Masters, and
Assessment Blackline Masters in the Unit Resource
Guide are on the Teacher Resource CD.*

Supplies for Each Student

ruler

Developing the Activity

Students can work on these problems individually, in pairs, or in groups. Students may complete them all at once or you can distribute them throughout the unit. Students must decide when it is appropriate to estimate and when it is appropriate to find an exact answer.

Suggestions for Teaching the Lesson

Homework and Practice

Assign some or all of the problems for homework.

Extension

Ask students to write their own problems. Have students swap problems with a partner. After students have solved their partners' problems, they can check each other's solutions and strategies.

Focus on Word Problems

Solve the following problems. Show how you found each answer. You will need a ruler and a copy of *Centimeter Graph Paper* to complete Question 8.

1. One Saturday, 37 people volunteered to help restore a prairie. The team leader wanted to place at least 5 people on each team.
   A. How many teams were there?
   B. How many people were on each team?

2. Mrs. Hix is planning for Girl Scout Camp. Each troop can send 15 members and there are 15 troops coming to camp. About how many Girl Scouts can she expect at camp? Explain your solution.

3. The Girl Scouts are going to Springfield to visit the state capitol. There are 23 girls in the troop. Each car can carry no more than three girls and a driver. How many cars are needed? Explain how you know.

4. Beverly collected 728 pennies. She sorted them into 3 jars. Which jar would you choose if she let you keep one? Explain why you chose that jar.
   A. The first jar had as many pennies as the "2" stands for in 728.
   B. The second jar had as many pennies as the "7" stands for in 728.
   C. The third jar had as many pennies as the "8" stands for in 728.

5. Write a story for this multiplication sentence: $24 \times 3 = ?$

6. Jenny measured the perimeter of a quadrilateral (a shape with four sides). Two sides were 8 centimeters long each. The other two sides were 19 centimeters long. What is the perimeter of the quadrilateral? Write a number sentence to show how you solved the problem.

7. Max found the mass of a box of crayons. He used ten 20-gram masses, five 10-gram masses, one 5-gram mass, and three 1-gram masses. What is the mass of the box of crayons?

Student Guide - Page 176

8. Caroline loves fruit. She eats four pieces of fruit every day.
   A. Copy her data table on a separate sheet of paper and fill in the missing data.

D Number of Days	F Pieces of Fruit
1	4
2	8
3	
4	

   B. Graph Caroline's data on a piece of *Centimeter Graph Paper*.
   C. How many pieces of fruit will Caroline eat in 9 days? Show how you found your answer on the graph.

9. Mrs. Reynold's class collected aluminum cans for the recycling drive. On Monday they had 436 cans. By Friday they had 712 cans. How many cans did they add to their collection between Monday and Friday?

10. This summer Fred and his father took a road trip. During the first week they traveled 487 miles. During the second week they traveled 346 miles. During their last week they traveled 279 miles.
   A. During the three weeks, estimate if they traveled more or less than 1000 miles.
   B. How many miles did Fred and his father actually drive?

Student Guide - Page 177

AT A GLANCE

Developing the Activity

1. Students solve the problems on the *Focus on Word Problems* Activity Pages in the *Student Guide.*

2. Students discuss their solution strategies with the class.

Homework

Assign some or all of the problems for homework.

Notes:

Student Guide

Questions 1–10 (SG pp. 176–177)

1. **A.** 7 teams

   B. 5 teams of 5 people and 2 teams of 6 people

2. Students need only an estimate. One possible strategy: $10 \times 15 = 150$ and $20 \times 15 = 300$, so there will be between 150 and 300 scouts at camp or about 200 scouts.

3.* $23 \div 3 = 7$ with 2 left over; 8 cars

4. B; Jar 1 has 20 pennies, Jar 2 has 700 pennies, Jar 3 has 8 pennies

5. Answers will vary.

6. $19 + 19 + 8 + 8 = 54$ centimeters

7. $10 \times 20 = 200$; $5 \times 10 = 50$; $1 \times 5 = 5$; $3 \times 1 = 3$;
   $200 + 50 + 5 + 3 = 258$ grams

8. **A.**

D Number of Days	F Pieces of Fruit
1	4
2	8
3	12
4	16

B–C.

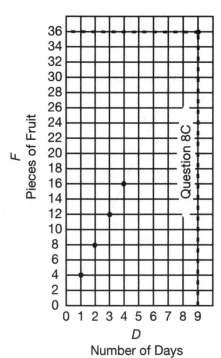

9. $712 - 436 = 276$ cans

10. **A.** more

    B. $487 + 346 + 279 = 1112$ miles

---

*Answers and/or discussion are included in the Lesson Guide.

**Answers for all the Home Practice in the *Discovery Assignment Book* are at the end of the unit.

Discovery Assignment Book

Part 1

Questions 1–6 (DAB p. 178)

1. 585
2. 603
3. 472
4. 382
5. Possible strategy: 872 is close to 900 and 490 is close to 500. So the answer is close to 900 − 500 = 400.
6. 252 marbles

Part 2

Questions 1–6 (DAB p. 178)

1. 142
2. 201
3. 247
4. 249
5. Possible strategy: 280 − 30 = 250 and 250 − 3 = 247.
6. **A.** Yes; 40 + 20 = 60; 43 and 29 are greater than 40 and 20
   B. 72 minutes or 1 hour and 12 minutes

Part 3

Questions 1–4 (DAB p. 179)

1. No, there are 42 people in the troop and the roller coaster can only hold 32 people.
2. 5 rides. 32 girls can ride in 4 rides but there are 3 girls left. Therefore it will take one more ride for all the girls to ride.
3. 21 bumper cars. 42 people in the group divide into 21 groups of 2.
4. **A.** Yes, the ride holds 45 people and there are 42 people in the group.
   B. 7 cars; 14 girls will ride with seven adults leaving 21 girls to ride without an adult. 21 is seven groups of three.

Part 4

Questions 1–2 (DAB p. 179)

1–2.

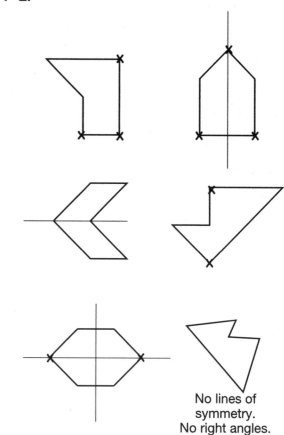

No lines of symmetry. No right angles.

*Answers and/or discussion are included in the Lesson Guide.